Cifras selectas de guitarra

Recent Researches in Music

A-R Editions publishes seven series of critical editions, spanning the history of Western music, American music, and oral traditions.

Recent Researches in the Music of the Middle Ages and Early Renaissance
   Charles M. Atkinson, general editor

Recent Researches in the Music of the Renaissance
   James Haar, general editor

Recent Researches in the Music of the Baroque Era
   Christoph Wolff, general editor

Recent Researches in the Music of the Classical Era
   Neal Zaslaw, general editor

Recent Researches in the Music of the Nineteenth and Early Twentieth Centuries
   Rufus Hallmark, general editor

Recent Researches in American Music
   John M. Graziano, general editor

Recent Researches in the Oral Traditions of Music
   Philip V. Bohlman, general editor

Each edition in *Recent Researches* is devoted to works by a single composer or to a single genre. The content is chosen for its high quality and historical importance and is edited according to the scholarly standards that govern the making of all reliable editions.

For information on establishing a standing order to any of our series, or for editorial guidelines on submitting proposals, please contact:

A-R Editions, Inc.
Middleton, Wisconsin

800 736-0070 (North American book orders)
608 836-9000 (phone)
608 831-8200 (fax)
http://www.areditions.com

RECENT RESEARCHES IN THE MUSIC OF THE BAROQUE ERA, 167

Santiago de Murcia

Cifras selectas de guitarra

Introduction, Transcription, and Critical Report

Edited by Alejandro Vera

A-R Editions, Inc.
Middleton, Wisconsin

A-R Editions, Inc., Middleton, Wisconsin
© 2010 by A-R Editions, Inc.

All rights reserved. No part of this book may be reproduced or transmitted in any form by any electronic or mechanical means (including photocopying, recording, or information storage and retrieval) without permission in writing from the publisher.

The purchase of this edition does not convey the right to perform it in public, nor to make a recording of it for any purpose. Such permission must be obtained in advance from the publisher.

A-R Editions is pleased to support scholars and performers in their use of *Recent Researches* material for study or performance. Subscribers to any of the *Recent Researches* series, as well as patrons of subscribing institutions, are invited to apply for information about our "Copyright Sharing Policy."

Printed in the United States of America

ISBN-13: 978-0-89579-678-3
ISBN-10: 0-89579-678-3
ISSN: 0484-0828

♾ The paper used in this publication meets the minimum requirements of the American National Standard for Information Sciences—Permanence of Paper for Printed Library Materials, ANSI Z39.48-1992.

Contents

Acknowledgments   vii

Introduction   ix

   The Composer and His Previously Discovered Sources   ix
   The Manuscript "Cifras selectas de guitarra" and Its Context   xiv
   The Music   xx
   Notes on Performance   xxxiii
   Appendix   xxxv
   Notes   xxxix

Transcription and Translation of the Preliminary Texts

   [Apuntes elementales de teoría musical]   3
   [Instrucciones para afinar la guitarra en relación con otros instrumentos]   4
   Explicación para facilitar la ejecución en aquellas cosas más estrañas de estas obras   5

Transcription of the Music

   1. Jácaras por la E   11
   2. Marionas por la B   12
   3. Difrencias de gallardas por la E   14
   4. Pavanas por la E   15
   5. Españoletas por la E   17
   6. Folías españolas por la E   18
   7. Jácaras francesas por la D   20
   8. El Amor por la E   21
   9. Tarantelas por la E   22
   10. Las vacas por la E   23
   11. Folías despacio al estilo de Italia   26
   12. Pasacalles de compasillo por la E   31
   13. A proporción por este tono   32
   14. Villanos por la C   34
   15. Caballero por la C   35
   16. Paradetas por la C   36
   17. Canarios por la C   38
   18. Menuet fácil   39
   19. Menuet   39
   20. Otro [Menuet]   40
   21. Otro [Menuet]   40
   22. Otro [Menuet]   40
   23. Otro [Menuet]   41
   24. Otro [Menuet]   41
   25. Otro [Menuet]   42
   26. El menuet inglés   42
   27. Menuet   42
   28. Otro [Menuet]   43

29. Otro [Menuet]   43
30. Otro [Menuet]   43
31. Otro [Menuet] difícil   44
32. Otro [Menuet]   44
33. Otro [Menuet]   45
34. Otro [Menuet]   45
35. Jácaras de la costa   46
36. El torneo por la C   47
37. La Azucena por la E   49
38. Los imposibles por la D   50
39. Cumbé por la A   52
40. Zarambeques por la C   53
41. Obra por la C   54
42. Bailad caracoles por la C   57
43. Marsellas por la B   58
44. Canción   60
45. Marcha de los oboes   60
46. Marcha valona   60
47. Marcha de los carabineros   61
48. Marcha de las guardias de la Reina Ana   62
49. Paspied nuevo   63
50. Burée por la D   63
51. Gavota   64
52. Gavota   64
53. Idea nueva, y obra especial de clarines   65
54. Obra por la K3   71
55. Burée   73
56. Pasacalles de compasillo por la O   74
57. A proporción   75
58. Pasacalles de compasillo por el +   76
59. A proporción   78
60. Pasacalles de compasillo por la B   79
61. A proporción   80
62. Pasacalles de compasillo por la G   81
63. A proporción   83
64. Pasacalles de compasillo por la D   84
65. A proporción   86
66. Pasacalles aclarinados por la C a compasillo   87
67. Pasacalles a compasillo por la H   89
68. A proporción   90
69. Pasacalles de compasillo por la A   91
70. A proporción   92

Critical Report   95

   Editorial Policies   95
   Critical Notes   101
   Notes   105

Acknowledgments

Beginning to write these acknowledgments, I cannot help but recall Michael Lorimer's expression of gratitude to Santiago de Murcia in his facsimile edition of "Códice Saldívar no. 4." I confess that I was a little struck by such a particular way of starting an academic work. Yet today, for some reason, I feel compelled to follow in his footsteps. Thus, I am grateful first to Santiago de Murcia for the music he composed, arranged, borrowed, and gathered in "Cifras selectas de guitarra," and for giving me the chance of undertaking such enthralling research. And I apologize to those who feel as struck by this word of thanks as I was after having read Lorimer's prologue.

I am indebted to several people at the Pontificia Universidad Católica de Chile for their help during my research and their positive response to my proposal of purchasing the manuscript. I am especially thinking of Carmen Peña, who helped me in the negotiations I undertook for that purpose, and also of Jaime Donoso, Eduardo Figueroa, Alejandro Guarello, Octavio Hasbún, Oscar Ohlsen, and the rector, Pedro Pablo Rosso. I also benefited from the invaluable aid of the staff of the Biblioteca Campus Oriente, namely Gloria Olea, Marcela Rivera, María Isabel Vásquez, Yanina Chandía, and Carola Tepper.

This research was partly supported by the Pontificia Universidad Católica de Chile (project VRAID n°03-II/05CCA) and the National Commission for Scientific and Technological Research from Chile (CONICYT, Project FONDECYT 1071121). I also thank the staff of the main libraries and archives I visited in Santiago, Chile (Archivo Histórico del Arzobispado, Archivo Franciscano, Archivo Nacional Histórico), Madrid (Archivo General del Palacio Real, Archivo Histórico de Protocolos, Archivo Histórico Diocesano, Archivo Parroquial de San Sebastián, Biblioteca Nacional) and Seville (Archivo General de Indias).

Several musicologists and performers contributed in one way or another to this research. Álvaro Torrente deserves special mention for his friendship and professional guidance, and also Juan Jorquera for his help in looking through some sources in the Biblioteca Nacional de Madrid after I had already returned to Chile. I am also grateful to Susana Antón, Cristina Azuma, Juan José Carreras, José María Domínguez, John Griffiths, Cristian Gutiérrez, Tess Knighton, Germán Labrador, Begoña Lolo, Miguel Ángel Marín, Juan Carlos Rivera, Pablo Rodríguez, Víctor Rondón, Alfredo Vicent, and Leonardo Waisman, as well as my former students Jaime Canto, Laura Jordán, and José Manuel Izquierdo. Despite the distance in time, I would also like to mention Daniel Estrada, who introduced me to the performance of the guitar many years ago.

My parents, Pedro and Patricia, have been fundamental both on the personal and professional sides of my life, as well as my brother and sisters, Lorena, Olivier, and Andrea.

Finally, I would like to dedicate this work to my wife, Marcela, and my children, Javier and Marcelita, for their love and support on each step of this research. It would not have been possible without them.

Introduction

The manuscript "Cifras selectas de guitarra" (1722) of Santiago de Murcia (1673–1739) was found by the present writer in Santiago, Chile, during research undertaken between September 2003 and August 2004, the purpose of which was partly to locate musical sources from the seventeenth and eighteenth centuries in that city.[1] This edition presents a detailed study of this source and its music along with a transcription and critical report, as well as a complete facsimile provided separately.

The Composer and His Previously Discovered Sources

The history of Santiago de Murcia's reception by contemporary guitarists and musicologists reflects the contrast of light and dark (chiaroscuro) traditionally attributed to the art of his time. On the one hand, his music has been studied and recorded by renowned scholars and performers,[2] who have contributed to raising its profile in the context of the baroque guitar[3] and to making its diffusion possible among amateur guitarists and music lovers. On the other, his biography has remained in almost total darkness, illuminated only by his own claim of being the guitar teacher of Queen Marie Louise of Savoy on the cover of his earliest and only printed source, *Resumen de acompañar la parte con la guitarra* (1714),[4] an assertion recently confirmed by Nicolas Morales, who found two documents in the Archivo General del Palacio Real de Madrid proving that Murcia occupied that position at least from 1704 to June 1706.[5] Because of this lack of historical references, and intending to situate the source to be edited here in its context, I shall attempt to sketch a more complete biography of the composer grounded on several documents recently found in Madrid archives. I will include in this account an overview of the milieu in which he was active as a guitarist and also consider the three other sources of his music (the print *Resumen de acompañar* as well as the manuscripts "Passacalles y obras de guitarra" and "Códice Saldívar no. 4") that have so far been discovered.[6]

Until very recently, Santiago de Murcia was thought to be related to an important family of instrument makers of Madrid. This hypothesis held that his parents were Gabriel de Murcia, a *violero* of the queen's household towards the end of the seventeenth century, as well as *guitarrero* of the Royal Chapel,[7] and Juliana de León, the daughter of another *violero*, Francisco de León, whom she took the place of sometime after his death. Since their marriage took place about 1682, that year was proposed as Murcia's approximate date of birth.[8] This family seemed a logical choice for the guitarist, since it provided an easy explanation for his entrance into the queen's household, especially considering that Gabriel de Murcia was the nephew of Juan Hidalgo, a famous composer and harpist of the court in the second half of the seventeenth century. Hence the hypothesis was generally accepted as the most feasible alternative, and it was even presented as a fact in a recent and important study.[9]

Nonetheless, a document of the parish church of San Sebastián in Madrid demonstrates that Santiago was born on 25 July 1673, and that he was actually the son of Juan de Murcia and Magdalena Hernández, who lived on calle de Las Huertas.[10] Although almost nothing else is known about his parents, some later documents allow us to infer their humble position in society: Juan de Murcia made a declaration of poverty in 1715, mentioning Santiago, Bartolomé, and Matías as his three children and stating that he came from Guadalajara, a town near Madrid;[11] he was living with his wife, his son Matías, and his daughter-in-law, María del Campo, in a rented house owned by the Carmelite convent on calle del Candil when he died on 14 May 1721; Magdalena Hernández died as well only a couple of weeks later, and Matías de Murcia followed her in November 1722, after an extended illness, each leaving a declaration of poverty as well.[12]

In 1695, Santiago de Murcia married Josepha García, who was eight years older than him and came from the village of Valdemoro. According to the marriage registry, he had been living for five years on calle del Escorial (district of San Martín), in houses owned by Francisco Aspur. Before that, for nine years (that is to say, roughly from 1681 to 1690) he had been a parishioner of San Luis, living on calle de Santa Brígida, in houses owned by Joseph de Leyva.[13] This last statement is suggestive, because his brother Bartolomé declared in 1705 to have been a parishioner of San Martín "all his life," living on calle de La Chinchilla.[14] Given that he was born in 1682,[15] this would imply that Santiago de Murcia was separated from his parents when he was about nine years old. In that case, it seems likely that he was serving as a choirboy for some religious institution, since the church was the usual place for the musical upbringing of a child at that time.[16] In fact, aside from the Royal College of Choirboys (Real colegio de niños cantorcicos), joined to the Royal Chapel, there were a significant number of monasteries in Madrid that had chapels with singers and instrumentalists.[17] Another possibility is that Murcia was under the guidance of a music (or guitar) master. Craig Russell proposed Francisco Guerau as the most likely candidate,[18] not only because of the publication of his well-known guitar book in 1694,[19] but also because he was in charge of teaching music to the choirboys of the Royal Chapel from 1696.[20] Of course, even though we now know that Murcia was not a boy at that time, Guerau's name should not be discarded. But there certainly were other guitarists in Madrid who could also have taught him the instrument.[21]

While Santiago was not directly related to Gabriel de Murcia, he was in all likelihood related to the *violero* Antonio de Murcia, who came from Guadalajara and served that post in the queen's household as well,[22] being appointed as such in 1704, the same year in which Santiago officially began his service in the court. Also, through Juan de Murcia's declaration of poverty, we know that Santiago's grandfather was one Blas de Murcia, from Guadajalara, and there was a surgeon with that name in the court at the end of the seventeenth century; nonetheless, it seems that he was Blas Martínez de Murcia, who apparently was unrelated to our musician.[23] Thus, it would seem that Santiago de Murcia's entrance to the queen's household is not to be explained by his family contacts, at least not exclusively by them. Since he was twenty-two years old in 1695, he must have begun his career about that time—perhaps even before—and he probably was already a well-known guitarist by 1704. Therefore, I propose here that it was his prestige, as a result of a somewhat significant career as a guitarist from the end of the seventeenth century onwards, that allowed him to obtain such an important position, since at that time artists were hired and rewarded to a great extent because of their talent and fame.[24] If true, this fact would have another relevant implication: that our future efforts to locate more information, for example, about Murcia's connection with public theaters, ought to focus on the years before 1700, rather than concentrating solely on the beginning of the eighteenth century as has been done previously.

The following references to Murcia's life, which have been uncovered so far, come from the two documents found by Morales in the Archivo General del Palacio Real de Madrid. The first includes payments to Murcia as guitar teacher from September 1704 to 1706; the second, dated 31 July 1708, reports a letter that he had written asking for his salary for the first semester of 1706, when he *served* his post ("por la asistencia que tenía de alicionar a Vuestra Majestad"). Based on this, Morales has proposed that Murcia was employed by the queen only until then,[25] which seems likely; nevertheless, her response, specifying that Murcia had to be paid "only for the first six months of 1706, as was done with his partner Mr. Diego Jaraba" (solo de los seis meses primeros del 706 como se ejecutó con su compañero Don Diego Jaraba),[26] casts some doubt on this proposal. It is clear that Murcia's teaching was interrupted in June 1706, when the troops of Archduke Charles entered Madrid and forced the court to move to Burgos, as part of the multiple events of the War of Spanish Succession; but there is no solid evidence against the possibility that his teaching resumed later. Be that as it may, the fact that Murcia did not go with the queen, unlike her singing teacher Francisco Larraz and her dance master Nicolas Fonton,[27] should lead us to wonder about his political position during that conflict. After all, the harpsichord teacher to the queen, Diego Jaraba, was suspected of betrayal for remaining in Madrid.[28] This might also have been the case for our guitarist, as suggested by two of the pieces edited here (nos. 37 and 48, as discussed below).

Murcia reappears in 1714, with the publication of his aforementioned *Resumen de acompañar*. Despite the date on the cover, the Spanish composer Antonio Literes wrote its official approval in 1717. Literes signed it in Madrid but stated that the book was "opened" in Antwerp. As Monica Hall explains, this in all likelihood indicates that it was printed there (*abierto* meaning "engraved"), which would place Murcia in the Low Countries about 1714.[29] Murcia presents himself on the cover as the guitar teacher of Queen Marie Louise of Savoy, but, given the information contributed by Morales, this does not necessarily mean that he worked as such until her death in February 1714, as previously thought. The book also includes an extended dedication to Jacome Francisco Andriani, an Italian aristocrat who resided in Madrid in the first half of the eighteenth century. Murcia declares his gratitude to Andriani for making it possible for his music to move from his drafts "to the smoked lights of the press" (de la oscuridad de mis borradores, a las ahumadas luces de la prensa), which probably means that Andriani financed the printing of the book.[30] Because of the closing of the dedication—"from this your house" (de ésta su casa)—it has been suggested that Murcia was living with Andriani at that time.[31] Nevertheless, this expression might be a variant of another that was very current in Spanish, which had a different meaning: "my house is yours" (mi casa es su casa; or: ésta es su casa). On the other hand, the *Planimetría general de Madrid* indicates that Andriani owned three pieces of land with houses before 1750.[32] Therefore, it is also possible that Murcia was not living with him but rather renting a house that Andriani owned. All the same, the dedication reveals a close connection between the two men and suggests that our guitarist was in Andriani's service. The prefatory pages close with a laudatory poem by Francisca de Chavarrí, who declares she is Murcia's admirer ("apasionada y favorecedora suya"). According to Russell, she was the daughter of Charles II's "proto-doctor."[33] All of this points out the influential contacts that the guitarist had, something that almost certainly helped him to a large extent in promoting his own work, as we shall see.

In the musical sphere, the importance of the *Resumen de acompañar* is well known. The first section of the book consists of an accompaniment treatise for the guitar, including a complete explanation of how to accompany a figured bass both in "natural" and "high" clefs, as well as a selection of musical examples in different meters and modes; according to James Tyler, it could be considered the most important treatise of the time for that instrument, along with Nicola Matteis's *The False Consonances* (1682).[34] The second part is a compilation of dances in guitar tablature, mainly of French origin ("La mariée," "La Bourgogne," etc.), most of which were taken from the anthologies published by the dance-master Raoul Auger Feuillet in Paris at the beginning of the eighteenth century.[35] The *Resumen de acompañar* is the first Spanish guitar source that shows such a predominance of that repertory,[36] and this feature is undoubtedly related to the cultural and political context in which it was produced: though the openness to foreign music did not begin in 1700,[37] the widespread circulation of French dances in Madrid at the beginning of the eighteenth century was undoubtedly increased by the arrival and personal tastes of Philip V and his wife. Even if the former apparently had no musical training, he was surrounded during his childhood by the intense musical life of the French court, knowing and appreciating the work of relevant composers, such as Campra and a young Destouches. During his trip to Spain at the end of 1700, his entourage included the count of Ayen, a music lover who assembled twenty-nine French musicians for accompanying the king up to the Pyrenees, and it seems possible that some of them followed him to Madrid. Thus, it is not surprising that Philip V requested his own French musicians a short time after his arrival at the Spanish court, engaging Henry Desmarets as director of his chamber music.[38] In addition to alleviating homesickness, the preservation of a similar musical environment was an important sign of identity and distinction for nobility when they moved to a different culture.[39]

While Desmarets's presence was for some reason ephemeral—he left Madrid in December 1706—French music was still performed in the circle of the queen, who had in her service since 1702 the French dance-master Nicolas Fonton and, several years later, the violinist Jacome Clair, who entered the queen's household in 1712.[40] It is very likely that Fonton utilized Feuillet's anthologies for his dance lessons for the queen, and it is not daring to imagine Murcia accompanying him with his own versions of those dances on the guitar. In fact, since Feuillet's books only included the violin part of each dance, the addition of at least one harmonic instrument was essential for its performance. Considering this, the hypothesis of Nicolás Morales about an eventual "aversion" of the queen to French music is unconvincing.[41] While it is true that Marie Louise of Savoy surrounded herself mainly with Spanish musicians (Jaraba, Larraz, Murcia) from 1704, the music they performed seems not to have been exclusively Spanish.

Of course, the French influence was not circumscribed only to the court. At least since 1713 the account books of the Madrid public theaters of La Cruz and El Príncipe show the frequent practice of finishing some comedies with a *contradanza* (Spanish name for the French *contredanse*); for example, on 29 November 1713, in La Cruz, a *contradanza* by "Navas" (Salvador de Navas) was performed for the *zarzuela* "No basta en amor lo fino."[42] So it is clear that Murcia's *Resumen de acompañar* reflects the extensive use of French dances both in the private sphere of the court and Madrid's urban spaces at that time.

Foreign (French, Italian) influence by no means implied an extinction of Spanish genres. Murcia included some Spanish pieces in his *Resumen de acompañar* as well, such as "Marizápalos" (p. 100), "Marsellas" (p. 107), and "Tarantelas" (p. 111).[43] All of them show the traditional structure of a theme and variations (hereafter also *diferencias*, in accordance with Spanish terminology), which Murcia mastered as well as anyone. Obviously, the proportion of foreign to Spanish music in this book does not correspond to what was being performed in Madrid around 1714. Murcia himself admitted in his prologue, added in 1717, that he deliberately refused to include *pasacalles* because of their extended cultivation, and the existence of numerous examples in previous works such as Guerau's *Poema harmonico*. Nonetheless, this explanation seems doubtful given that Murcia would include many settings of this genre in his later sources, so that his decision might be interpreted as an attempt to identify his book with aristocratic circles, an aspect to be discussed later in this study.

While the previous paragraphs develop some features of this source that have been dealt with somewhat by other scholars, such as Russell and Hall, the biographic information supplied here allows us to glimpse another point: the *Resumen de acompañar* is a mature work, published when its author was forty-one years old, a relatively advanced age at that time. Therefore the book collects, especially in its first section (the accompaniment treatise), the extended knowledge acquired by the guitarist during his career. And, of course, this is even more true for two other of his sources, the first of which—the manuscript "Passacalles y obras de guitarra"—is dated 1732.[44] Unlike Murcia's previous book, this one combines mainly suites (*obras*) in the French and Italian style with Spanish *pasacalles* in different modes, alternating duple and triple meter. Although lacking specific attributions, some of its pieces in the French style belong to other composers such as François Campion, Francesco Corbetta, and the Belgian François Le Cocq,[45] as demonstrated by Hall and Russell. But the only composer mentioned by Murcia is Arcangelo Corelli, some of whose sonata movements are transcribed for guitar in "Passacalles y obras."[46] In contrast, the *pasacalles* were apparently written by Murcia himself.

The second of these two other sources of Murcia is the manuscript "Códice Saldívar no. 4," which was discovered by the Mexican musicologist Gabriel Saldívar in León (Guanajuato) in 1943.[47] Actually, it lacks any indication of author, title, or date, but Michael Lorimer has clearly established its relationship to Santiago de Murcia on the basis of its resemblance to "Passacalles y obras" with regard both to format and copyist.[48] Additionally, its first page includes a *décima* (a Spanish kind of verse) that serves as a dedication, but it is undoubtedly a riddle alluding to the guitarist himself, since the initial letters of the two first lines are *S* and *M*.[49] With respect to the music, "Códice Saldívar" mainly includes Spanish dances (*bailes* and *danzas*),[50] such as the *jácaras, marionas,* and *españoletas,* along with some others of African influence—such as the "Cumbé" and "Zarambeques"—which were cultivated in Portugal, Spain, and the New World since at least the seventeenth century. There are also some French dances ("Fustamberg," "Cotillón") and a sonata in three movements, of which the second is clearly written in Corelli's style.[51]

While Lorimer's argument about the relationship between Murcia and the "Códice Saldívar" is conclusive, his proposal that both this manuscript and "Passacalles y obras" represent two volumes of a single anthology perhaps requires further reflection, especially because the former has been dated to 1732 on the basis of this proposal. As we have seen, the title of "Passacalles y obras" clearly reflects the musical content of the book, composed of *pasacalles* and suites; on the contrary, the "Códice Saldívar" has a totally different makeup. Besides, the first movement of the abovementioned sonata in "Códice Saldívar" (fols. 91r–92r) is included as well in a suite of "Passacalles y obras" (fols. 71v–73r) with minimum variants, which may lead us to wonder why two volumes of a single anthology would include the same piece. Be that as it may, the resemblance between both sources with respect to the format (for example, with four staves per page) and handwriting makes it likely that "Códice Saldívar" was compiled at a time very close to "Passacalles y obras." Moreover, we shall see additional data supporting—though not confirming—Lorimer's conjecture when we examine the music of the main source edited here.

Another puzzling aspect of these manuscripts is their relationship to Mexico. In addition to being the place where the "Códice Saldívar" was found, "Passacalles y obras" was purchased there by Julian Marshal before it arrived at the British Library (Add. Ms. 31640), a fact that led Hall and other scholars to propose that Murcia might have traveled to the New World at the end of his life, thus explaining the apparent difficulty in finding any information about him in Madrid after 1717.[52] This conjecture seemed to be strengthened by some additional facts: a copy of the *Resumen de acompañar* belonging to the Los Angeles Public Library was probably acquired in Mexico by Cornelius F. Borton;[53] the manuscript Ms. 1560 of the Biblioteca Nacional de México had some concordances with the *Resumen de acompañar*;[54] and the latter was cited by Juan Antonio de Vargas y Guzmán in his guitar book, of which two copies are dated Veracruz (Mexico), 1776.[55]

Nonetheless, two new documents linked with Murcia, which I have found in the Madrid archives, weaken, to a large extent, the conjecture that he took these sources to or copied them in Mexico: his declaration of poverty and his death certificate. The guitarist made the first of these on 2 July 1729, just days after the death of his wife, Josepha García.[56] Despite its brevity, this document affords important details on Murcia's life. He apparently had no children, since he designated his niece, Josepha Palacios, as his only heir. This fact may be surprising if one considers that in his aforementioned letter to the queen, reported in 1708, he declared that both he and his wife had been sick for five months and were suffering hardship for having "a large family to maintain" (mucha familia que mantener).[57] Therefore, in spite of the ambiguous character of this expression—he could be referring to his parents or brothers—it is possible that Murcia's children died after 1708. In that case, the fragment of the dedication in the *Resumen de acompañar* hinting at his "adverse luck" (adversa suerte) might be interpreted as a deliberate complaint about this tragedy.[58]

Returning to the hypothetical trip to Mexico, his declaration shows that in 1729 he resided in Madrid in the district of the parish church of San Martín, specifically on calle de La Salud, in houses owned by the Carmelite convent.[59] Given that his death certificate shows that he died on 25 April 1739 and was still living in the same city and house,[60] it seems extremely unlikely that he traveled to Mexico in about 1732, taking "Passacalles y obras de guitarra" there. On the contrary, this new evidence clearly indicates that the sources for Murcia's music were produced in Madrid and subsequently sent to Mexico. Fortunately, his declaration of poverty also provides some potentially significant details on that topic:

> ... and likewise he pleads to Srs. Pedro Juan and Íñigo de Garay y Cochea, Sr. Joseph de Quesada and Sr. Manuel de Pereda, to whom he asks for the love of God that they do what they can for the good of his soul, and they must be handed over the music papers that the grantor owns, in commemoration of the great love that he has had for them.[61]

Although I have not been able to identify Joseph de Quesada, one Manuel de Pereda requested a certificate in 1709 for having accompanied Marie Louise of Savoy to Burgos (1706),[62] which places him in the court when the guitarist worked there. He probably was the same man who in 1695 entered the Order of Santiago.[63] But the most interesting data involve Pedro Juan and Íñigo de Garay y Cochea (or Garaicoechea). The first was a knight of the Order of Santiago (a commonplace among Murcia's acquaintances) who was born in Manila, Philippines, about 1690. His parents were General Juan de Garaicoechea, who was stationed in Manila at the end of the seventeenth century, and María Magdalena de Villarreal, native of that city.[64] The second was Pedro's half brother, who entered the Order of Santiago in 1711. He was born in Manila in 1695 and his mother was the second wife of Juan de Garaicoechea, Teresa María de Aróstegui, native of Cadiz. The most significant fact: from about 1700 until 1711 he lived in Mexico with his family.[65] Although currently I cannot state precisely the time at which Pedro and Íñigo moved to Spain, the former already resided there in 1714, since in that year he obtained permission to take merchandise to Honduras on the condition that he returned the profits to Spain.[66] In any case, both were living in Madrid when Murcia made his declaration of poverty, as proven by several documents of 1727–30 belonging to them, including their last wills.[67] In the latter, they declared themselves to be "residents" in Madrid, but Íñigo hinted at his estates "in the Indies." His half-brother was even more precise when he declared his capital on 17 July 1729,[68] stating that he owned an *encomienda* in the Philippines[69] and had a right to 463,500 *reales de vellón* in the house of his father "in the city of Mexico." In other words, the fact that Murcia partly bequeathed his music papers to Pedro and Íñigo de Garaicoechea could be connected to the preservation of "Passacalles y obras" and the "Códice Saldívar" in Mexico. Even though this statement remains conjectural, these two brothers represent the first direct contact identified so far between Murcia and Mexico.

The extract cited above demonstrates that towards the end of his life Murcia had close contacts with some aristocratic individuals, as he did many years before with Jacome Francisco Andriani and Francisca de Chavarrí. Though the current stage of research does not allow us to determine exactly the kind of relationship he had with Quesada, Pereda, and the Garaicoecheas, it seems likely that they were Murcia's students and supported him in some way. After all, teaching guitar must have been an important way of surviving for a musician who certainly was not connected with the court after 1714 (perhaps earlier). This hypothesis reminds us of the mature character of all his known sources, something true for the *Resumen de acompañar*, but especially for "Passacalles y obras," dated 1732, when he was almost sixty years old, and possibly the "Códice Saldívar" as well. In all likelihood both manuscripts were produced in a period when the guitarist was less active as a performer than as a teacher of particular people. This immersion in the private sphere would explain why his name tended to disappear from the public archives (Palacio Real, Archivo de Villa), making more difficult the location of biographical information about him.

Two concordances between Murcia's music and the anonymous "Libro de diferentes cifras de guitara" (1705),[70] mostly unnoticed by other scholars, might throw some additional light upon these conjectures. The first is a *pasacalle* "por 2o. tono" in triple meter included in both "Passacalles y obras" (fols. 45v–46v) and the "Libro de diferentes cifras" (pp. 48–51). Despite some variants and the different order of the first variations, there is no doubt that these are two versions of the same piece (example 1).[71] The second concordance involves the well-known "Cumbés" included in the "Códice Saldívar" (fol. 43r) and the "Paracumbé" of the "Libro de diferentes cifras" (p. 46). While both pieces are different in this case, it is no coincidence that their strummed introductions are very similar, given the particular chords they contain (example 2).[72]

Since Murcia was the guitar teacher to the queen in 1705 and consequently the most important guitarist in Madrid, and the "Libro de diferentes cifras" was copied there and included guitar music by "the best composers," as stated on its cover (escogidas de los mejores autores), it seems very likely that the anonymous copyist gathered some of Murcia's pieces in his book. Therefore, this source seems to confirm that the music of Murcia was already known at the beginning of the eighteenth century, and that he was a prestigious musician when he entered the court. But these concordances, especially the first, also suggest that the guitarist included some pieces in "Passacalles y obras" and the "Códice Saldívar" that

Example 1. Beginning of the *pasacalle* "por 2o. tono" in "Passacalles y obras" (fol. 45v) and the "Libro de diferentes cifras" (p. 48). The numbers indicate correspondences between the variations.

Example 2. Beginning of the "Cumbés" in "Códice Saldívar no. 4" (fol. 43r) and the "Paracumbé" in "Libro de diferentes cifras" (p. 46). The Xs indicate a percussive effect on the guitar soundboard (or strings?).

he had composed or arranged many years before, a fact that supports the hypothesis that his manuscripts were produced after the heyday of his career.

All of this significantly changes some of our previous assumptions about Murcia and his work. Since his manuscripts were not copied in Mexico, but rather in Madrid, the music they include was also composed there, something true even for those pieces that have been supposed to be American or Mexican, such as the "Zarambeques" or "Cumbé."[73] After all, these and other "African" dances appeared almost simultaneously in coastal cities of the Congo and Angola, the Iberian Peninsula, and Latin America,[74] and they were well known in Madrid at the beginning of the eighteenth century, as proven by their common presence in the theater.[75] While Murcia possibly attempts in his versions to capture the rhythms and sonorities of their African or African-American models (perhaps not literally reproducing but developing or parodying them), such models had been mediated for many years by their involvement in Spanish culture. Both these and other foreign (French, Italian, Belgian) pieces gathered by the guitarist thus reflect the multiculturalism and cosmopolitanism in the capital of Spain at that time, a feature that gave rise to hybrid styles and genres, an interesting aspect to be discussed below. Although Murcia could have traveled to France or even America during his life—the evidence supplied here is not enough to discard these ideas, though it clearly brings the composer nearer to Spain than to other places—he was not obliged to do so in order to assemble pieces reflecting the influence of several regions and continents. This perspective changes the emphasis of the questions currently posed about Murcia, from asking about an eventual or particular trip of the composer to considering more generally the circulation of Spanish guitar music and its reception in the New World; and this latter will be a key issue when we examine the source presented in this edition.

Finally, the fact that Murcia bequeathed his music papers to four of his acquaintances may throw light upon the status of a musician in eighteenth-century Spain. While it is true that when a musician died his heirs sometimes demanded the property of his scores as material objects, instead of as works in abstract terms,[76] they frequently did it because of an interest in the music itself.[77] Consequently, musicians held an inherent status as artists, somehow independent of their social condition, which may explain the frequent hardship they suffered despite their considerable renown.[78] Murcia did not ascribe a specific value to his papers—he declared himself to be in absolute poverty—but he was aware of the intrinsic worth of the music they contained.

The Manuscript "Cifras selectas de guitarra" and Its Context

Description

The manuscript "Cifras selectas de guitarra" (1722) was preserved in the bookshop of César Soto (calle Merced) but had previously belonged to Alfredo García Burr, a collector who owned an important number of objects of art and books in his private residence, known as the "Casa de los Diez."[79] After García Burr's death, the collection was auctioned by his heirs in the auction house Enrique Gigoux Renard, where César Soto bought the manuscript on 30 November 2001. The inventory of the books auctioned reflects the value of the more than six thousand volumes in García Burr's personal library and also shows that he had some interest in music, though to a lesser extent than in other disciplines.[80] After extended negotiations I undertook at the end of 2004, the manuscript was acquired by the Pontificia Universidad Católica de Chile and is currently in one of the university's libraries, the Biblioteca Campus Oriente, still uncatalogued.

In general terms, it is a book in oblong format (24 x 16.5 cm) and bound in leather, in an excellent state of preservation, which might indicate that most of the time it was treated as a collection item rather than as a practical book, although this by no means implies that it was never used for performance by a guitarist. Both the name of its composer and the date are indicated on the front cover, with the latter showing a correction (the insertion of *D* to indicate MDCCXXII; see the facsimile). The attribution to Santiago de Murcia is certain both because of the musical content and the striking resemblance of the manuscript to "Passacalles y obras" and "Códice Saldívar" in terms of the format and main copyist.

The tight binding makes it difficult to determine the codicological structure of the manuscript exactly without risk of damaging it. However, this is also because the manuscript is apparently composed of little gatherings mostly assembling two sheets. In spite of this, the book can be divided into at least three major parts: (1) the initial section, including the cover (with the inscription "Castilló," a possible owner, of whom we shall speak later) and two folios, one of a smaller size with elementary notes on music theory, and another with instructions for tuning the guitar in relation to other instruments (harp, bandurria, violin, and tiple); (2) a middle section of three folios, including the table of contents and a prologue entitled "Explanation to facilitate the execution of the strangest things in these works" (Explicación para facilitar la ejecución en aquellas cosas más estrañas de estas obras); and (3) seventy folios with guitar pieces in tablature, forming the main part of the manuscript. This last section is written on the same type of paper, since all the folios share a single chain line measurement (roughly 3 cm) and watermark—an *S* linked to a *P*, to be discussed below (figure 1). Parts 2 and 3 clearly were copied by the same hand, as can be seen from a comparison between some of the titles in the table of contents and the musical section of the manuscript.[81] This copyist is apparently the same who wrote the music in "Passacalles y obras" and "Códice Saldívar," as suggested by a comparison between the quoted facsimiles of both manuscripts and "Cifras selectas de guitarra."

The table of contents reveals that the manuscript originally consisted of eighty-five folios, of which unfortunately the last fifteen have been lost, along with the pieces they included: "Obra [suite] de alemanda, correnta, y giga por la E";[82] "Obra de Coreli, de alemanda, correnta, zarabanda, y giga por la E"; "Otra obra de Coreli, de grave, o preludio, alemanda y dos gigas por el +"; and "Difrentes [i.e., diferentes] piezas por la B" without further specification. Of all these titles, it is possible to be certain that the "grave, o preludio" corre-

Figure 1. Main watermark in "Cifras selectas de guitarra" (fol. 60r).

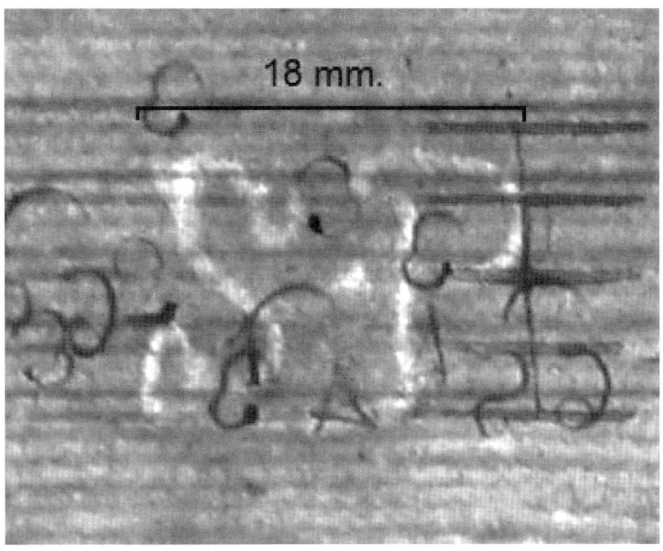

sponds to the "grave" of the "Tocata de Coreli" included in "Passacalles y obras" (fol. 86r), given that its third measure is cited by Murcia as an example in the prologue of "Cifras selectas de guitarra." Notwithstanding, the titles of the remaining movements do not coincide with those of the "Tocata." In addition, folios 33, 42, and 44 are missing, with the complete loss of "Canarios por la A" and "Paspied viejo," and the partial loss of "Los imposibles por la D" (no. 38 of the transcription), "Cumbé por la A" (no. 39), "Marcha de las guardias de la Reina Ana" (no. 48), "Paspied nuevo" (no. 49), and a gavotte (no. 52). But the fact that almost all these pieces are concordant with others found in different sources makes it possible to complete the lost fragments. Finally, folio 44 must have been mostly unwritten, since according to the table of contents it did not include anything other than the end of a gavotte beginning on folio 43v (no. 52). In other words, the music section was in turn divided into two large parts, the first including single pieces, mostly in Spanish style, and the second containing suites and *pasacalles* in different modes. It is even possible that each part formed a single manuscript in a first stage, and they were joined to compile a more extended anthology.

It seems that what I have identified as the middle section was added to the musical part at a later time. Apart from being on different paper, the prologue was apparently written on pages previously used for correspondence (the upper right hand corner of its last folio shows the greeting "Muy Sr. Mío"), something that might denote its circumstantial nature and perhaps even that it was written in haste. In fact, in the list of contents (first page, second column) three pieces—"Paradetas por la C," "Canarios por la C," and "Menuet fácil" (nos. 16, 17, and 18)—appear in reverse order, which does not seem to be explained by a disorder of gatherings, nor anything like that. In addition, the first folio of the musical section is slightly stained and darkened in comparison to the others, which would be explained if it had formed the beginning of the book for some time.

On the other hand, the first section seems to have been added later than the other two. The cover was written with a different handwriting and on another kind of paper, since its watermark, which does not reappear in other folios, consists of three circles grouped vertically, the first topped with a cross, the one in the center having the letters C, B, and R, and the lowest one with a letter O, or a circle, inside it. Regarding the two folios with notes on music theory and tuning, the former is smaller in size and the second has a "9" in the upper right-hand corner, indicating that both corresponded to later inclusions and probably came from other sources. Their presentation is also much less careful than the rest of the manuscript and the handwriting does not correspond to the main copyist.

Aside from the intrinsic value of "Cifras selectas de guitarra," the presence of a new copy of *Resumen de acompañar* bound with it confers even greater interest on that source. To my knowledge, it is the fourth copy known of Murcia's first book—the others are preserved in the Biblioteca Nacional de Madrid, the Newberry Library (Chicago), and the Los Angeles Public Library.[83] This copy does not contain the aforementioned prologue to the reader by Murcia nor the approbation written by Antonio de Literes in 1717. As Hall explains, both of these are contained in a bifolium that was inserted between the front page and the dedication three years after the book was printed.[84] Following her conjectures, Russell has suggested that only then was it made available to the public,[85] but the fact that both the edition attached to "Cifras selectas de guitarra" and the copy in the Los Angeles Public Library do not contain that section might indicate that the *Resumen* circulated before 1717. Additionally, pages 80–81 are missing from this latest copy, and the front page includes the inscription "Ortega" at the bottom, possibly another owner.

Context of Production

Although with the current state of research the precise conditions of production for "Cifras selectas de guitarra" are uncertain, on the whole, the information presented above relates it to Madrid. Santiago de Murcia was certainly living there from 1729 to 1739, and all the previous references to him come from that city: his birth in 1673, his marriage in 1695, his entrance to the court about 1704, and the approbation of his *Resumen de acompañar* by Literes in 1717. Only the printing of this book might relate him to Antwerp in 1714, but even if this is true, this fact would probably imply nothing but a transitory displacement there. Hence both "Passacalles y obras" (1732) and "Códice Saldívar no. 4" were in all likelihood copied in the capital of Spain, and nothing indicates that it was different for our manuscript.

On the other hand, while the main watermark of "Cifras selectas de guitarra" (see figure 1) is the same as that which appears in "Passacalles y obras" and "Códice Saldívar no. 4," in the latter, at least, its size is larger by one centimeter.[86] Such a significant change seems to be explained by a considerable distance in time,[87] supporting the hypothesis that "Códice Saldívar" was copied about 1732, a decade later than "Cifras selectas."

According to Jan LaRue this paper originated in Genoa but had wide circulation in Spain.[88] Genoese paper also reached Chile in the eighteenth century, as proven by the account books of religious institutions.[89] But, above all, it was commonly used for copying music in the Royal Chapel in the second quarter of the eighteenth century, since the *SP* watermark is found in some *villancicos* by the chapel master Francisco Corselli, copied in the 1740s.[90] Consequently, while this watermark in itself would not be enough to relate the production of "Cifras selectas" to a precise geographical context (Genoa, Spain, or even Chile), the *villancicos* by Corselli, along with the biographical evidence presented above, allows us to relate its presence to Madrid.

An additional fact supporting this hypothesis is that all of Murcia's manuscripts share the same handwriting. It is possible that the copyist was Murcia himself,[91] but there are some aspects pointing in another direction. Though the copy of "Cifras selectas de guitarra" is extremely elegant and careful, its version of "Las vacas por la E" (fol. 11r [no. 10]) lacks the third measure, something that would have been evident for Murcia. Likewise, in "Zarambeques por la C," measure 39 (fol. 35r [no. 40]), there is a G indicated on the open third course instead of the fourth, which produces an unacceptable dissonance. Granted, we all know the incredible mistakes we can commit when we write any extended text. However, there is an additional case that seems difficult to attribute to tiredness: measure 98 of "Paradetas por la C" (fol. 23r, third measure of the fourth line in the facsimile [no. 16]) indicates to play both the unfretted fifth (A) and fourth (D) courses together in the third beat, resulting in a very unusual sonority for ending a scale in Murcia's music. At the same time, the next measure (m. 99) lacks the first beat. Since the latter is a repetition of measure 95 in a lower octave, it is obvious that the A on the fifth course actually corresponds to the first beat of measure 99 and was incorrectly placed by the copyist (example 3). This mistake could be explained if this fragment had been copied from a draft in which the positions of both notes were not clearly indicated, by someone who did not possess sufficient knowledge of the notational system for placing them appropriately. This leads me to suggest that "Cifras selectas de guitarra," as well as other Murcia manuscripts, could have been written by a professional copyist active in Madrid who might have been paid by the guitarist or one of his supporters. Although the identity of this eventual collaborator is uncertain, we know at least the names of the copyists of the Royal Chapel at the beginning of the eighteenth century, who represent likely candidates for this task: Manuel Pérez (1701–13), Juan Simón Barber (1701–15), Felipe Zafaro (1715–24), Isidro Montalvo (1715–51), Gabriel Andrés Martínez (1717–30), Tomás Laína (1730–35), and Agustín de Cuéllar (1731–51).[92] The only secure example of Murcia's handwriting—his signature in his declaration of poverty—is not enough to confirm or discard the hypothesis that the manuscript was copied by someone else. Nevertheless, we have to admit that the similitude between his *S* and that of some inscriptions in "Códice Saldívar" casts doubt on it.[93]

Example 3. Copy mistake in "Paradetas por la C" (fol. 23r [no. 16, mm. 95–100]).

Another clue apparently connecting the manuscript to Madrid is found in the first section, particularly in the abovementioned folio including instructions for tuning the guitar in relation to other instruments. Actually, these instructions are taken, at least partly, from *Reglas y advertencias generales*, published in Madrid by Pablo Minguet e Yrol.[94] The fourth paragraph, indeed, corresponds almost literally to the eleventh rule of Minguet's chapter dedicated to the guitar,[95] while the fifth paragraph was taken from the twelfth rule.[96] Since this book appeared about 1752–54, this concordance confirms the presence of a different handwriting and the later inclusion of this page, establishing a *terminus post quem* for it. Nevertheless, it is not certain that the cover was added to the manuscript at the same time (it could have been added before).

All the same, the addition of both the first and middle sections at a later stage of compilation than the music may throw light on the conditions of production of the manuscript, especially because it is not an exclusive feature of "Cifras selectas de guitarra." In "Passacalles y obras" the cover and table of contents seem to have been adder later by another person,[97] and in "Códice Saldívar" the cover is missing and the table of contents unfinished.[98] In my opinion, it is possible that Murcia had these manuscripts prepared without front pages or contents with the purpose of adding these parts when they were sold; that way it would be possible to accommodate the title and a dedication to the recipient, or even allow the latter to write an inscription himself (for example indicating his property of the source). In fact, the same purpose may explain the notable changes on the covers and dedications present in Foscarini's guitar books, printed in Italy in the first half of the seventeenth century.[99] According to this hypothesis, the year on the cover of "Cifras selectas" could indicate that the manuscript was sold or sent to a recipient in 1722, but not necessarily copied then.

This last assertion leads us to the apparent character of the manuscript as a book for sale. Unlike "Passacalles y obras," which is specifically dedicated to one Joseph Álvarez de Saavedra,[100] Murcia addresses the prologue of "Cifras selectas de guitarra" to a hypothetical amateur. This approach is reminiscent of the prologue of *Resumen de acompañar*,[101] which, as a printed source, was not intended for a particular recipient, but for distribution among a wider range of music lovers. Consequently, it seems that "Cifras selectas de guitarra," instead of being a personal gift, was also intended to circulate in some context with commercial purposes. And despite the absence of any specific reference to that context, I believe that other paragraphs of the same prologue, as well as an examination to some contextual aspects, may allow us to raise some alternatives at least in a speculative way, which constitutes the aim of the next section.

Finally, although the date of the manuscript might be somewhat problematic, I think there is no reason to consider 1722 invalid as an approximate date. Furthermore, the version of the abovementioned *pasacalle* "por 2o. tono" included in "Passacalles y obras" is much more similar to that of "Cifras selectas de guitarra" (fol. 54r [no. 57]) than the version in "Libro de diferentes cifras" (compare example 1 to the transcription of that piece in the present edition), which seems to bring our manuscript nearer to 1732 than 1705. In other words, "Cifras selectas" can also be considered as a mature source, produced by Murcia after the heyday of his career. Likewise, this concordance with the "Libro de diferentes cifras" (we shall see others later) indicates that the manuscript, as well as "Passacalles y obras" and "Códice Saldívar," apparently included some pieces composed or arranged by the guitarist many years before. In this manner, the commercialization of these sources might have represented a way to survive in a period when he was less active as a performer.

Hypotheses on the Circulation and Reception of the Manuscript

Since the possibility that "Cifras selectas de guitarra" was copied in Chile has been discarded in the previous section, the question that arises is whether it arrived there during the eighteenth century or more recently. Of course, the response would not alter the importance of this source for the history of the baroque guitar, but it could have a bearing on its significance for the colonial American world. Although a definitive response is lacking, this section is intended to supply some elements for deeper reflection on that topic. There is evidence indicating that while "Cifras selectas de guitarra" was produced *in* Madrid it was not intended *for* that city. Indeed, the discovery of the manuscript in Chile is not an isolated fact, since both "Passacalles y obras" and "Códice Saldívar no. 4" appeared in Mexico. This suggests that all these manuscripts were explicitly sent to different regions of Hispanic America by Murcia himself. Otherwise, we ought to accept that their arrival in that continent was the product of later and independent events, which would represent an extraordinary (though possible) coincidence, especially considering that no manuscript by Murcia has been found in Spain. The fact that Alfredo García Burr never traveled abroad, but gathered his whole collection in Chile by buying directly from private owners at auctions, also reinforces this hypothesis.[102] But perhaps the most significant clue is contained in the prologue of *Resumen de acompañar*, in which Murcia explains the reason he did not include any explanation whatsoever of the symbols he used to represent the ornaments on the guitar:

> I will not stop to explain the graces there are in playing either, which are the salt of the performance (despite their virtual notation), persuaded that there will be no amateur who has not seen such a singular book given to print as that of Don Francisco Garau (of the sounds of Spain and exquisite pasacalles), in which he gives a full explanation at the beginning, with noteworthy clarity and knowledge, for whoever wishes to play this instrument; with all the ornaments that pertain to this last skill.[103]

Murcia clearly took for granted that in Madrid and surrounding areas any amateur would know the symbols used by Guerau and himself for the ornaments. Therefore, when he decided to add a detailed explanation of them in the prologue of "Cifras selectas de guitarra," it is very possible he did so because he expected that the manuscript would be received somewhere else, where amateurs might ignore their meaning. This is reminiscent of the image of Hispanic America that another guitar author, Lucas Ruiz de Ribayaz, projected in the prologue of his *Luz y norte musical* in 1677, which Murcia must have been familiar with. According to Ribayaz, in "different kingdoms and remote overseas provinces" (he had formed part of the entourage of the Count of Lemos when the latter traveled to Lima in 1667) people did not know or practice the guitar tablature "or any other ciphers" because they played "by memory," with the exception of a few who knew musical notation.[104] In fact, Murcia explained not only the ornaments but also the duration of basic rhythmic figures in duple meter. This suggests that the prologue of "Cifras selectas" was written with the inhabitants of that continent in mind. If true, the fact that the guitarist did not include a chart with the *alfabeto* system seems to be explained because it was already contained in the *Resumen de acompañar*, bound along with the manuscript.

The preparation of a guitar manuscript for commercialization in Latin American colonies should not be surprising in a period when there was a relatively constant passage of music books to that continent. At least two references related to the guitar are contained in a document in the Archivo General de Indias (Seville), including the inventories of books presented to the Inquisition for their approval to be dispatched to America. The earliest is the shipment to New Spain in 1699 of the aforementioned *Luz y norte musical* by Ruiz de Ribayaz.[105] The second is an inventory of the books presented on 17 November 1723 by the presbyter Joseph Juárez de Estrada and sent to Tierra Firme, which includes a book entitled "Zifras de guitarra" by an unspecified author.[106] Though the reference is too general to state that it referred to our manuscript, it is noteworthy that it occurs on a date very close to that which appears on the cover of "Cifras selectas." Apart from guitar books, the Inquisition records document the sending of some theoretical treatises in the late seventeenth and early eighteenth centuries: *El porqué de la música* by Andrés Lorente (1672), on several occasions; *Música universal* by Pedro de Ulloa (1717); *Fragmentos músicos* by the Franciscan Pablo Nasarre (1683, 1700); and Joseph de Torres's *Reglas generales de acompañar* (1702, 1736) and *Arte de canto llano . . . y arte práctico de canto de órgano* (1705).[107]

Not surprisingly, sending such books was frequently promoted by the composers themselves: in 1704 the organist Joseph de Torres sent four chests to Cartagena and New Spain with his masses and treatise on accompaniment (*Reglas generales de acompañar*).[108] This consignment was endorsed by the council of the king and was in that way free from being examined by the Inquisition, which demonstrates the importance of having influential contacts for these commercial activities. Murcia was not an exception in this respect: in the first section of this introduction I documented the significant contacts that the guitarist had with Mexico, which might be linked to the preservation of some of his music there. But what was the case for a somewhat peripheral region such as Chile, which apparently was more isolated from Spain? Although, as with other points, more conclusive evidence is lacking, it is possible at least to document an important connection between Jacome Francisco Andriani, who probably contributed to the printing of the *Resumen de acompañar*, and Santiago de Chile. On 4 August 1717 the Franciscan friar Juan Murillo, custodian of the great monastery of that city, wrote a letter to Andriani from Buenos Aires, just after returning from Spain, where he had traveled to vote in the general chapter of his order.[109] The familiar tone of the letter, with affectionate regards to "Señor Ambrosio, my young ladies, the children, and all the family" (el señor don Ambrosio, mis señoritas, los niños, y toda la familia) denote a quite close relationship between them. This is also true of a second letter written by Murillo on 28 March 1718, this time from Santiago de Chile, recommending the new governor, Gabriel Cano de Aponte.[110] The mention of "Señor Ambrosio" is interesting because one Ambrosio Andriani, envoy of Lorena, was apparently involved in the arrival of the well-known Italian composer, Giovanni Battista Mele, in Madrid in 1732, to serve as music teacher to the duke of Osuna's daughter.[111] Thus, it is possible that Jacome Francisco was not the only member of his family interested in musical patronage. He was also well-connected to other places in South America: on 26 August 1711, Esteban Ferrer, a knight of the Order of Santiago who resided in Lima, empowered him and other men to be in charge of his judicial affairs.[112] In other words, Murcia did not lack a contact for sending his music to that continent and even to Chile, though it is not possible to affirm that Andriani was directly involved in the arrival of "Cifras selectas" there.

Until now, I have not found any reference to the sending of music books specifically to Chile, though I can supply a spectacular piece of information in the field of instruments: in 1722 the Jesuits Lorenzo del Castillo and Manuel de Ovalle were authorized to ship, among other things, "thirty-one large and small chests containing five organs" (treinta y un cajones chicos y grandes que contienen cinco órganos) for their missions in Chile.[113] But the arrival of music books from the Iberian Peninsula is demonstrated by their presence in the inventories in Santiago de Chile, both of private people and religious institutions. The inventory of Andrés de Rojas y Lamadris (1775) includes an "Arte de música" in Portuguese, possibly the *Arte de musica de canto dorgam, e canto cham* (Lisbon, 1626) by Antonio Fernandes; and the inventory of José Cabrera (1798), canon of Santiago Cathedral, shows a book of plainchant by "Roel" (probably the *Institución harmonica, ò doctrina musical, theorica, y práctica, que trata del canto llano, y de órgano*, published in Madrid, 1748, by Antonio Roel del Río) and Antonio Soler's *Llave de la modulación* (Madrid, 1762).[114] Likewise, around 1767 the Jesuit college of San Miguel owned Zarlino's *Istituzioni armoniche*, and the library of the Franciscan convent of Santiago included Pablo Nasarre's *Escuela música según la práctica moderna* (Zaragoza, 1723–24) in 1799.[115]

In any case, the arrival of a guitar manuscript in the eighteenth century would coincide with the widespread use of this instrument in colonial Chile. We have found it in the hands of people from different social conditions and ethnic groups. For example, Josepha Díaz Herrera owned a "big guitar" along with a harp in 1701; Ignacio Hurtado also possessed a harp and a guitar when he died in 1774; and Manuel de Besanilla held two "common guitars" on his ranch next to Santiago in 1777. There is even an eye-catching "red guitar from China" (guitarra de china colorada) mentioned in the will of a well-off woman, María Josefa del Solar, in 1723,[116] and the instrument also appears in the will of the Indian Andrés Samaya (1689), native of the northern village of Huasco.[117] A brief look at religious institutions is even more instructive: around 1676 the Mercedarians held a noteworthy group of wind and string instruments, including two guitars, and a guitar was the only instrument used in the little church of their ranch in Huaquén in the middle of the eighteenth century;[118] about the same time, the Jesuit mission of San Cristóbal, next to the town of Concepción, owned a guitar and a violin;[119] and from 1680 to 1686 the Franciscan constitutions show several prohibitions regarding having and playing the guitar, finally giving way in 1689 to an authorization to the *vicario de coro* (the person responsible for music in the monastery) to play it when necessary.[120] With these precedents, it is totally natural that in 1789 there was a guild of guitar builders (*guitarreros*) in Santiago de Chile,[121] the only musical guild of that city in the colonial period that has been documented so far. Likewise, guitar strings seem to have been the sole musical object exported from Chile at the end of the eighteenth century.[122]

In spite of the attractiveness of the hypothesis that the manuscript was sent to Chile by Murcia or someone else during the eighteenth century, we have to admit the existence of some potential arguments against it. The first could be the abovementioned signature of one "Castilló" (or Castillo, since possibly the accent was not essential to that name) on the front page. While I have not been able to identify this owner, I have found a very plausible candidate: Felipe del Castillo Albo, a Spanish man who traveled from Cadiz to Lima in September 1803 to market fabrics.[123] Despite his apparent intention of returning to Spain, he had to remain some time in Peru and moved to Chile later, certainly before 1810, since in May of that year he married Manuela Irigoyen in Santiago.[124] We find him in several documents from the first half of the nineteenth century, all of them from Santiago de Chile, until his death in that city on 2 March 1840.[125] What is significant about him is the striking similitude between the flourish of his signature and that on the cover of "Cifras selectas de guitarra," despite some differences in the handwriting (figures 2a and 2b). The facts that the manuscript appeared in Chile and that a Castillo, whose rubric is similar to that of "Cifras selectas," was living there in the early nineteenth century are perhaps no coincidence. In that case, the manuscript could have reached Chile about 1803–10, if he actually brought it from Spain (or Lima); but it is also possible that he purchased it when he was already living in Chile, though, once again, both alternatives are conjectural.

Another fact apparently opposed to an early arrival of the manuscript is the abovementioned presence of some notes taken from Minguet's *Reglas y advertencias generales* in its first section. Since this book appeared in Madrid about 1752–54, it would seem that the manuscript was still there at that time. Nonetheless, it is also possible that the notes were made somewhere else, since we have already seen that Spanish music books circulated in Hispanic America throughout the colonial period, and it could be the case of Minguet's as well.

A further objection may be that if Murcia's manuscript had reached Chile or South America in the eighteenth century, it seems strange that there is no evidence of the influence of his music there, unlike in Mexico, where some of the pieces gathered by him are disseminated in other sources apart from his own. However, I have found an interesting concordance, previously unnoticed, which might make up for this scarcity of data. There is a book for guitar in Lima (Museo Nacional de Historia) from the late eighteenth century, the first part of which contains pieces in guitar tablature and the second written with conventional notation. It includes thirty-one pieces, mostly of Spanish origin, of which twenty-nine have been edited by the guitarist Javier Echecopar, whose description I am referencing here. This manuscript belonged to Jorge Tambino, apparently a priest who lived until the beginning of the nineteenth century, and Francisco García, a military man ("Teniente coronel del Real Cuerpo de Ingenieros") who bought it in 1805.[126] The first piece transcribed by Echecopar (p. 10), a minuet, corresponds undoubtedly to a "Menuet de trompas" included in "Códice Saldívar no. 4" (fol. 83r).[127] The variants in the version from Lima mainly consist of the sub-

Figure 2a. Felipe del Castillo Albo's signature, in Contaduría mayor, 1ª serie, vol. 1102, fol. 312r, Archivo Nacional Histórico (Santiago de Chile). Courtesy of the Archivo Nacional de Chile.

Figure 2b. The signature on the cover of "Cifras selectas de guitarra."

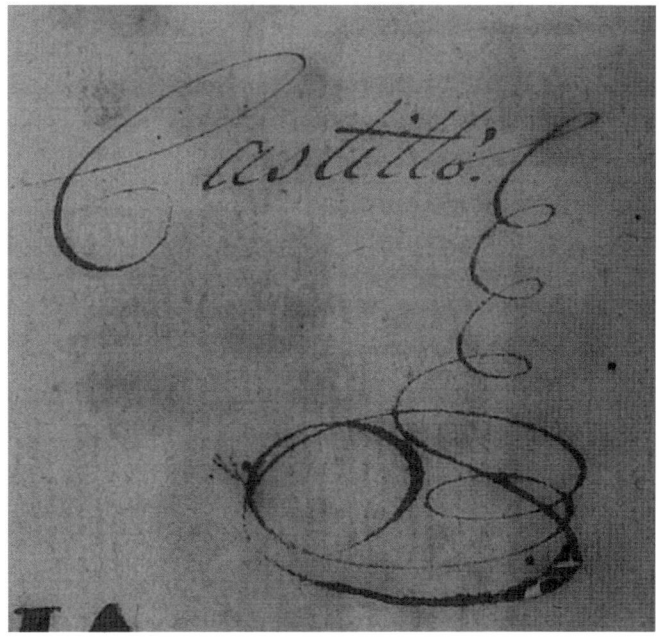

stitution of some chords by others in the middle of each part, and the appearance of some triplets instead of binary rhythms in the second part, which reflects the style of the later epoch in which this version was made. Obviously, both Murcia and the anonymous compiler of this manuscript might have copied this minuet from another independent source or other sources, since it is not clear at all to what extent the minuets gathered by Murcia belong to him. Also, the "Menuet de trompas" does not appear in "Cifras selectas de guitarra," which would have represented a clearer clue of its presence in South America in the eighteenth century. However, I think it ought to be seriously considered that this concordance reveals a wider influence of Murcia on that continent than suggested only by the appearance of "Cifras selectas." After all, if Murcia's music could reach Chile during the colonial period, it would be surprising that it did not arrive in Peru, which occupied a more central position in colonial administration. This question, as well as others dealt with before, is still to be studied more deeply in the future, but I do believe that the information discussed in this section suggests that the current presence of "Cifras selectas de guitarra" in Chile is not merely coincidental.

The Music

Notation and Theory

The notational system used by Murcia has been approached in several studies and "Cifras selectas de guitarra" does not present any novelty pertaining to it.[128] Nevertheless, it is worth summarizing here the main traits so as not to oblige the reader to consult another work on such an essential topic.

Murcia's music is notated in the so-called Italian tablature, which actually was both Spanish and Italian. In that system the five courses of the guitar (tuned e', b, g, d, A, as in the modern instrument) are represented by a five-line staff, in which the bottom line corresponds to the first course. The fret and course that are to be pressed are indicated with a number placed on a line, 0 representing an open course, 1 the first fret, and so on. Murcia represents the tenth fret by a roman numeral (x), but the upper frets (not frequent) are again represented by arabic numbers. Additionally, until folio 26v Murcia places dots near each number to specify the left-hand fingering: a single dot indicates that the fret must be pressed with the index finger, two dots refer to the middle finger, and so on. The significant implications of this practice for performance will be discussed later.

In passages in plucked style, the duration of notes is indicated above the staff with conventional rhythmic figures. Each value applies both to the number placed below and to those that follow, until the appearance of a new rhythmic figure. When two or more notes are played at the same time, the rhythmic value applies at least to one of them, but the others can be sustained. The sustaining of some notes can also be given by a fixed position of the left hand, as when performing rapid arpeggios—an example is found in the last variation of "Folías despacio al estilo de Italia" (fols. 18r–18v [no. 11]). Murcia uses oblique lines across the staff to indicate this, though in a very inconsistent way, since many such passages lack this symbol. On the other hand, a horizontal line under the staff indicates a *barré* chord or scale: the index finger must be placed on the lowest fret of the passage spanned by the line. Nonetheless, Murcia is not consistent here either, as shown by a comparison between "Cifras selectas" and the concordant passages in his other sources. In addition, he uses a stylized barline to demarcate the variations within each piece, a symbol that also might indicate an optional repeat, depending on the musical context.[129] A half double barline is used to separate the sections in binary dance types (see, for instance, the minuets of fol. 27r and following). Sometimes, a pair of dots is placed on each side of that symbol, indicating the repetition of both sections (see the minuets on fols. 25r–26r). But it is not clear whether the absence of dots implies that such repetition is optional or whether they were omitted due to an oversight by the copyist. The half double barline is also used occasionally to separate the variations beginning on the upbeat, which end in the middle of measures (see "Pavanas por la E," fols. 4v–5r [no. 4]).

The strummed chords can be notated with the system described above (numbers on the staff lines) or with the so-called *alfabeto* (or *abecedario*) system for the guitar. In fact, the latter consists merely of representing a given chord using a letter of the alphabet instead of using numbers on the staff lines to represent each pitch of that chord. Murcia offers two unabridged charts for the *alfabeto*, one in *Resumen de acompañar* (p. 5) and the other at the beginning of "Códice Saldívar." Example 4, however, includes only the symbols that he uses in the pieces of "Cifras selectas." Sometimes, in *barré* chords, a number is placed above the letter indicating that it must be played on a fret other than the first. In strummed chords notated either with numbers or the *alfabeto* system, their rhythmic value is shown by a stemmed note placed to their right and inside the staff. A downward stem indicates a downward strum (i.e., from the lower to the upper string, since the bottom line of the staff represents the first course), and vice versa.

All but one of the symbols indicating the ornaments are thoroughly explained by Murcia in the prologue, and they virtually correspond to Guerau's *Poema harmonico*. This similitude allows us to make up for the absence of any explanation of the symbol #, which indicates an ornamental vibrato.[130] The remaining ornaments are the slur (*extrasino*), mordent (*mordente*), and trill (*trinado*). Murcia places the slur below the numbers in ascending scales, and vice versa, in order to facilitate the understanding of it by beginners. He also uses it for notating the appoggiatura, by placing two slurred numbers in the space spanned by a single rhythmic figure (see, for example, "Jácaras por la E," fol. 1r [no. 1, m. 2]). In cadences, the appoggiatura is often followed by a mordent, a formula equivalent to the French *port de voix et pincé*. Murcia, not surprisingly, is the first Spanish guitarist to utilize this ornament, reflecting the multicultural context in which he was active.[131] Although the slur is written down in the same way as in current practice, the mordent is indicated by a comma (,) and the trill by a particular symbol (✗). Murcia specifies the fret corresponding to the upper auxiliary note of the trill with a number placed below the ornament. He also explains its execution with clarity, but this aspect is to be commented on later.

As regards meter, "Cifras selectas" includes only a few time signatures, which, fortunately, had been explained by Murcia himself in the *Resumen de acompañar*.[132] The triple meter is highly predominant in the manuscript and Murcia notates it with the Spanish symbol of the "proporción," a 3 or a stylized Z (see, respectively, "El Amor por la E," fol. 9v [no. 8], and "Marionas por la B," fol. 2r [no. 2]). Such a time signature was used in Renaissance practice to indicate a change from duple to triple meter in a given voice. Thus, it was a *proportional* sign, showing that three notes were to be sung in the time of two. This

Example 4. Letters of the *alfabeto* used by Murcia in "Cifras selectas de guitarra." It is worth noting that in my transcriptions of the pieces, most of these chords are written in root position. For an extended discussion of this policy see "Voicing" in the editorial policies of the critical report.

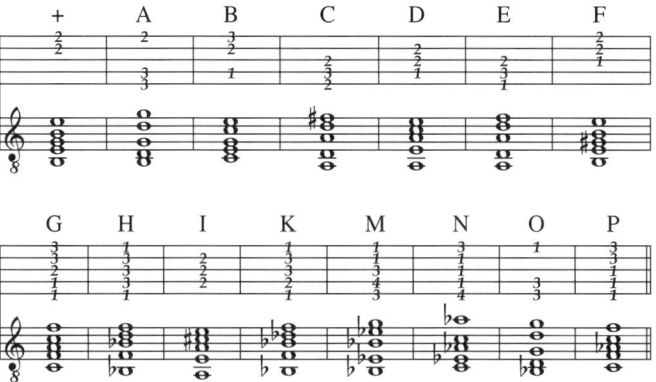

proportion was called "proporción sexquiáltera mayor" when it involved whole notes (*semibreves*) and "proporción sexquiáltera menor" when it involved half notes (*mínimas*), *sexquiáltera* implying the ratio 3:2. During the seventeenth century (and even earlier) *sexquiáltera* began to be used in all the voices of compositions at the same time and ultimately acquired a complete autonomy, giving rise to two independent ternary meters, the "compás [or *tiempo*] de proporción menor" and the "compás de proporción mayor." In the former, each measure was composed of three half notes, and, in the later, of three whole notes.[133] Murcia's *Resumen* demonstrates that, at the beginning of the eighteenth century, the abbreviated name "proporción" was used to indicate virtually any kind of triple meter, since he declares that each measure can be composed of three whole, half, or quarter notes.[134] "Cifras selectas," indeed, reflects this practice: although in most of the pieces with the time signature Z or 3 the meter is equivalent to the modern 3/4 time, the "Correnta" of the "Obra por la K3" (fol. 51v [no. 54]) is written in 3/2 and the "Zarambeques por la C" (fol. 35r [no. 40]) are written in 3/8. This last case undoubtedly denotes Murcia's intention that the piece be performed very rapidly.[135] Yet Murcia uses the modern time signature 3/4 in two minuets (fols. 26r–26v [nos. 25 and 26]), though according to *Resumen de acompañar* (p. 43) it was virtually equivalent to the "proporción."

The other time signature very common in "Cifras selectas" is 𝄴, equivalent to the *compasillo*. As the modern 4/4 time, it is composed of four quarter notes with the difference that it was intended as a duple meter divided into two half notes (the downbeat and upbeat, or "dar" and "alzar").[136] Murcia makes a distinction between two kinds of *compasillos*, one called "de nota negra" (of the quarter note) and the other "a medio aire" (in middle tempo). The former was similar to our 4/4 time, since it was performed slowly and, in consequence, the quarter notes acquired a greater importance. The *compasillo* "a medio aire" was performed somewhat faster, so that the quarter notes could be dissonant with more liberty.[137] Nasarre, who designated the two kinds of *compasillo* as "de nota negra" and "de nota blanca," argues that the former frequently used quarter and eighth notes, while in "nota blanca" the whole and half notes were more common.[138] These two types of *compasillos* seem to be represented in "Cifras selectas" by pieces such as "Pavanas por la E" (fol. 4v [no. 4]), with its abundant sixteenth notes, and "Caballero por la C" (fol. 21r [no. 15]), where the shortest figure is the eighth note.

Murcia also utilizes the symbol ¢ in two *burées* (fols. 43r and 52v [nos. 50 and 55]) and two gavottes (fol. 43v [nos. 51 and 52]). Although, according to Spanish theory, each measure should be composed of two whole notes, these pieces are virtually written as a fast *compasillo* (i.e., in a current 2/2 time), something that Murcia accepts as a legitimate practice in *Resumen de acompañar* (p. 42). This can be related to the French style of those pieces and foreign influence in general, which contributed to the modification of musical practice and theory in Spain.[139] Additionally, in the "Marcha de las guardias de la Reina Ana" (fol. 41v [no. 48]) Murcia indicates the time signature 2, which was not commented on in the *Resumen*. Francisco Valls considers it as equivalent to the modern 2/4 time, but a foreign author (Jean-Baptiste de Castillion) describes it as a meter also composed of four quarter notes but performed even faster than ¢.[140] This seems to be the case for the "Marcha," denoting, once again, the great extent to which foreign music influenced our guitarist.

Finally, Murcia utilizes 6/8, 6/4, 12/8, and 6/9 time signatures, which were considered proper for modern music in his time. These meters originated from the *sexquiáltera* proportion explained above,[141] since they also supposed the ratio 3:2. For instance, 12/8 indicated that twelve eighth notes should be performed in the time of eight (i. e., in the time of a *compasillo*). Murcia uses this meter in the brief "Fajina" (fol. 48r, a section of "Idea nueva, y obra especial de clarines" [no. 53]) and the ending of three *pasacalles* in duple meter (fols. 60v, 63r, 66r [nos. 62, 64, 66]), a formula that Neil Pennington sees as a sort of hybridization.[142] As proven by *Resumen de acompañar*, Murcia considered 6/8 and 6/4 as equivalent time signatures, unlike his contemporary theorists.[143] Consequently, even though the "Tarantelas por la E" (fol. 10r [no. 9]) and the "Canarios por la C" (fol. 23v [no. 17]) are indicated, respectively, with 6/8 and 6/4, both are actually written in 6/8 time. The 6/9 or "sexquinovena," indicating that nine eighth notes must be performed in the time of six, is used a single time, in the conclusive section of "Las vacas por la E" (fol. 12r [no. 10]).

A final aspect to be dealt with here is the modal system used by Murcia. He lists eight "tonos naturales" or natural modes (example 5) in *Resumen de acompañar*, indicating possible transpositions for each one.[144] These modes roughly coincide with those listed by Spanish theorists such as Lorente, Nasarre, and Joseph de Torres.[145] But there is a significant difference concerning the eighth mode, since these authors held that its key signature had no accidentals. They accepted, however, that this mode could finish either on the "final" (main note) or the "mediación" (secondary note), that is, on C (example 6). While Nasarre declared at the end of the seventeenth century that the two endings were equally common,[146] Murcia's cadence in the eighth mode (example 5) shows that he always finished it on the "mediación," given that the F-sharp in the key signature makes its structure

Example 5. Cadences of "tonos naturales" in Murcia's *Resumen de acompañar* (pp. 10–11).

Example 6. Eighth mode finishing on the main note (G) and the "mediación" (C).

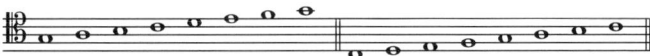

Example 7. Modal melodies in "Cifras selectas": "Jácaras por la E" (fol. 1v [no. 1, m. 45]); "Pavanas por la E" (fol. 5r [no. 4, m. 30]); "Las vacas por la E" (fol. 21v [no. 10, mm. 100–101]).

equivalent to a C scale. In this manner, he equalized modes 5, 6, and 8 in a single structure equivalent to our major mode. This seems to confirm from a theoretical point of view the impression that one has when listening to his music: that it roughly fits within the tonal system despite its use of a modal terminology. Furthermore, the only mode that Murcia avoids in "Passacalles y obras" is the fourth, the most distant from modern tonality. The pieces of "Cifras selectas de guitarra" also point in the same direction, since in those written "por la E," that is, in the first mode, the B is mostly flatted. In this manner, its structure is equivalent to a modern minor mode.

Nonetheless, we should not forget that most of the Spanish dances included in Murcia's sources had originated many years earlier. For example, the sequence I–III in the harmonic progression of "Difrencias de gallardas por la E" (fol. 3v [no. 3]) is not very idiomatic in the tonal system. Likewise, Murcia's melodies sometimes show modal traits, as can be seen in the fragments gathered in example 7, all of them taken from pieces written in the first mode. Thus, it is possible that totally equating Murcia's keys and modern tonality would result in a misunderstanding of his music, or at least in the partial loss of its character. For this reason, and although the point deserves to be studied more deeply, in the present edition I have preferred to refer to Murcia's key signatures with his own terminology based on the *alfabeto* system, such as "por la E" and "por la C," instead of with the modern concepts of D minor, D major, and so on.

General Contents

As we explained above (see p. xv), since the currently missing folio 44 was mostly unwritten, the music section of the manuscript can be divided into two subsections. In short, the first contains a varied repertory including mainly Spanish and French single dances, as well as a French suite, two *pasacalles*, and four marches. The second, on the other hand, includes in its present state fifteen *pasacalles*, two suites, and a single *burée*. However, the missing final folios also contained three additional suites (two by Corelli) and some unspecified pieces "por la B." Table 1 shows a classification of the repertory for the first subsection, including the pieces fragmentarily preserved, but not those entirely lost.

The present section is not devoted to a study of each genre in detail, both because it would largely exceed the purposes of an introduction and because Esses and Russell have already undertaken this task, presenting a good deal of information for most of them.[147] Nonetheless, it is indispensable to review some fundamental aspects. In general, each Spanish dance was characterized by an elemental and somewhat abstract harmonic progression,[148] which constituted a sort of theme for an undefined number of instrumental *diferencias* (example 8). This feature has at least four significant implications for Murcia's pieces in the Spanish style. First, its improvisatory nature: while this music is written down and therefore fixed in a manuscript source, such "fixing" may be considered as only transitory, something confirmed by the different versions of some dances that Murcia wrote during his life, as we shall see. Second, the concept of *work* in reference to these pieces is, at least in its traditional sense, inappropriate given its association with closed structures and single authorships,[149] which might help us to understand some processes of appropriation to be examined later on. Third, while the first measures of each piece might be considered as the theme itself, they actually correspond to the first variation, since the original and authentic theme—the *precursor*, we should say—was probably unknown to Murcia and his contemporaries, at least in the case of traditional dances such as the *jácaras* and *marionas;* so that we have here an example of the somewhat cryptic statement that Harold Bloom applies to the literary sphere, that the precursor of a poem may be a "poem that never got written."[150] And fourth, such music cannot be purely and simply identified with a written tradition, since it actually bears both oral (variable, undefined) and written (more fixed) components, despite its current state as a manuscript text.[151] In fact, the importance of oral transmission is raised by Murcia himself in a paragraph to be quoted later, where he declares that no explanation of the symbols used for the ornaments can replace the experience of listening to a good guitarist performing them, as well as the instructions he gives "verbally."

But the characterization of these pieces as a sort of written improvisation is also confirmed by the music itself, since most Spanish dances are actually unfinished, despite their apparent closing at the end. This is perhaps more obvious in "Códice Saldívar no. 4," where in fact some pieces, such as the "Fandango" (fol. 18r) and

TABLE 1
Contents of the First Musical Subsection of "Cifras selectas de guitarra"

Spanish Dances	French Dances	Others
Jácaras por la E (1r)	Menuet fácil (24v)	Pasacalles de compasillo por la E (18v)
Marionas por la B (2r)	Menuet (25r)	A proporción por este tono (19v)
Difrencias de gallardas por la E (3v)	Otro [Menuet] (25r)	Obra por la C (35v)
Pavanas por la E (4v)	Otro [Menuet] (25r)	Marcha de los oboes (40r)
Españoletas por la E (6r)	Otro [Menuet] (25v)	Marcha valona (40r)
Folías españolas por la E (7v)?	Otro [Menuet] (25v)	Marcha de los carabineros (40v)
Jácaras francesas por la D (8v)?	Otro [Menuet] (26r)	Marcha de las guardias de la Reina Ana (41v)
El Amor por la E (9v)?	Otro [Menuet] (26r)	
Tarantelas por la E (10r)	El menuet inglés (26v)	
Las vacas por la E (11r)	Menuet (27r)	
Folías despacio al estilo de Italia (13v)?	Otro [Menuet] (27r)	
Villanos por la C (20v)	Otro [Menuet] (27v)	
Caballero por la C (21r)	Otro [Menuet] (27v)	
Paradetas por la C (22r)?	Otro [Menuet] difícil (28r)	
Canarios por la C (23v)	Otro [Menuet] (28r)	
Jácaras de la costa (29r)	Otro [Menuet] (28v)	
El torneo por la C (29v)	Otro [Menuet] (28v)	
La Azucena por la E (31v)	Canción (39v)	
Los imposibles por la D (32r)?	Paspied nuevo [42v]	
Cumbé por la A [33v]	Burée por la D (43r)	
Zarambeques por la C (35r)	Gavota (43v)	
Bailad caracoles por la C (37v)	Gavota (43v)	
Marsellas por la B (38r)?		

Note. Dance titles set in roman type indicate *bailes,* while those set in italic type indicate *danzas;* some cases in which such distinction can be problematic are indicated by a question mark.

Example 8. Harmonic progression of "Marionas por la B" (fols. 2r–3v [no. 2]).

"Cumbé" (fol. 44v) lack the last measure.[152] But it is also true for "Cifras selectas de guitarra," where most of the Spanish dances finish with a figure shorter than a full measure in length, which does not always coincide with the beats omitted in the initial anacrusis and even occurs in pieces beginning on the downbeat. The explanation is that, in most cases, such as "Tarantelas por la E" (fol. 10v [no. 9]) and "Villanos por la C" (fol. 21r [no. 14]), the last note does not complete the anacrusis of the entire piece, but that of the last variation, as though the piece was inviting the performer to add additional variations to his own taste. In fact, the first piece of the manuscript in which the last note completes the entire measure is "Folías despacio al estilo de Italia" (fol. 18v [no. 11]). Since it is by far the longest piece in "Cifras selectas," with 272 measures, it is logical that Murcia wanted to *finish* it there.

Murcia's mastery in writing *diferencias* is well known. In general, he succeeds in avoiding any trace of monotony, among other things, by subtly introducing additional chords to the basic progression. Compare, for instance, the essential harmonic scheme with the fifth variation of "Tarantelas por la E" (no. 9) (example 9).

Example 9. Harmonic progression and fifth variation of "Tarantelas por la E" (fol. 10v [no. 9, mm. 17–20]).

In spite of the moderate use of an elaborate counterpoint (the pieces are written mainly in a free or two-voice texture; the strict use of three voices is occasional; a fourth note appears only in strummed chords and does not represent a new voice, but always fulfills a harmonic function), Murcia frequently combines different textures, provoking a coloristic contrast between consecutive variations. Measures 173–84 of "Folías despacio al estilo de Italia" (no. 11) exemplify this with a sudden transition from a variation requiring a masterful technique to a chordal one in which the melody of the upper voice, along with the dissonances and suspensions, give rise to a calmer but expressive atmosphere demanding a rather sensitive performance (example 10).

On the other hand, based on two *pasacalles* of "Passacalles y obras," Pennington has shown that Murcia organized their rhythmic structure by "increasing curves of activity/relaxation, reaching the climax at the end of

Example 10. "Folías despacio al estilo de Italia" (fol. 16v [no. 11, mm. 173–84]).

the piece."[153] Although this feature should not be used to characterize all of Murcia's *diferencias*, it is quite clear that it fits in well with many of them: "Jácaras por la E" (fol. 1r [no. 1]), "Las vacas por la E" (fol. 11r [no. 10]), and "Jácaras de la costa" (fol. 29r [no. 35]) are representative examples. These kinds of pieces are highly demanding from a technical point of view, with an abundance of scale passages in sixteenth notes, both slurred and in *campanelas* (i.e., performed in alternated strings), as well as frequent ornaments that are difficult for the left hand. But the increase of intensity pointed out by Pennington also depends sometimes on another factor: the gradual shift of the main melody to the upper register. In "Bailad caracoles por la C" (fols. 37v–38r [no. 42]), for instance, the d" is reached only in the third from last and penultimate variations (mm. 40–46),[154] though the register descends in the last one, ending in a sort of repose. A clearer example is "Paradetas por la C" (fol. 22r [no. 16]), where the highest pitch in the first variation is g', in the second a', in the third b', and in the fourth d". Likewise, in "Canarios por la C" (fol. 23v [no. 17]), the increase and diminution of the intensity is regulated both by rhythmic activity and the register, reaching the d" only from the middle of the piece onward (mm. 33 and 50ff.). On the whole, Murcia's *diferencias* give the impression of a careful organization of musical materials at different levels, resulting in exciting pieces both for listening and performing.

An interesting aspect of Spanish dances that connects them to their social context is the usual division in *bailes* and *danzas* at that time (the latter are indicated in italics in table 1). In general, the term *bailes* denoted dances associated with the lower classes and consequently were performed in a more exuberant manner, with expressive movements of the arms and hands, while the term *danzas* designated those associated with the aristocracy and were performed in a stylized and controlled manner, with movements mainly of the feet, but not the arms.[155] As Esses affirms, however, such distinctions are problematic, since "specific meanings and connotations vary among the sources of the 17th and early 18th centuries," and occasionally even a single dance is assigned to both categories by different authors.[156] In fact, in "Cifras selectas" there are some doubtful cases (indicated in table 1 by a question mark). Perhaps the most difficult is the term *folía*, since it was used from the sixteenth to eighteenth centuries to designate different kinds of dances. Esses synthesizes its history by affirming that, despite its popular origin, it was stylized by the early seventeenth century as an aristocratic *danza*. Nevertheless, in "Cifras selectas" Murcia presents two kinds of *folías*, Spanish and Italian ("Folías españolas por la E," fol. 7v [no. 6], and "Folías despacio al estilo de Italia," fol. 13v [no. 11]), whose origins are not clear. I have provisionally followed Russell's opinion, based on Richard Hudson's study of the genre, according to which the Spanish type resembles more the popular dance in beginning with an anacrusis, and the Italian type is related to its aristocratic counterpart in starting on the downbeat and sustaining each chord for an entire measure,[157] though the point is far from being clear. In other cases, the doubt is motivated by the lack of specific studies about a genre with the subsequent scarcity of information. An example is "El Amor por la E" (fol. 9v [no. 8]), a dance characterized by its modulating harmonic progression (although no other degree than the first reaches the status of a tonal center). Aside from its mention in "El maestro de arpa," an *entremés* from the end of the seventeenth century, and a musical setting contained in the "Libro de diferentes cifras," the only known reference to it is a call for its prohibition, along with other "obscene" dances, in 1733 and 1745 by the Bishop of Tervel (southern Aragon).[158] Two other dances that are difficult to classify are "Los imposibles por la D" (fol. 32r [no. 38]), which shares a common harmonic progression with the *vacas*, and "Marsellas por la B" (fol. 38r [no. 43]).[159] In contrast, the popular nature of "Bailad caracoles por la C" (fol. 37v [no. 42]) is suggested by one of the definitions of the word "caracol" in the dictionary of the *Real Academia Española* in 1729: "a certain movement executed in vulgar dances, with people walking around in single file" (cierta mudanza que se hace en los bailes vulgares, andando muchos alrededor unos detrás de otros).[160] Likewise, the "Jácaras de la costa" (fol. 29r [no. 35]) was a popular dance with a harmonic progression very similar to that of the traditional *jácaras*, but in major mode. Its name owes to its origin in Malaga; at least this is the information provided by the dictionary of the *Real Academia Española*.[161]

The distinction between *danzas* and *bailes* is even more problematic if one considers that some aristocratic dances may have gradually been adopted by the popular culture while at the same time some popular dances were appropriated by the elites. Murcia represents a clear example of the latter, since his *bailes* do not correspond to their original models danced by people in general, but rather to a parody of popular genres. We shall see, indeed, that the guitarist made an explicit attempt to differentiate between his own "delicate" technique and a more strident one, undoubtedly that of non-professional guitarists. Of course, this statement raises the importance of the performance (not only the musical content) in making such a difference. But it also has fundamental implications for the meaning that we currently assign to some pieces such as "Marionas por la B" (fol. 2r [no. 2]) and "Villanos por la C" (fol. 20v [no. 14]), for which the term *baile* is debatable in that sense. We have also shown in the first section that "Cumbé por la A" (fol. [33v] [no. 39]) and "Zarambeques por la C" (fol. 35r [no. 40]) were neither composed nor copied in Mexico, but in Spain, so that their characterization as "Mexican dances" was inappropriate. Nevertheless, they also are not transcriptions of the dances performed by the African slaves living in Madrid, but rather elaborate pieces inspired by "African music" in a wider sense.

In spite of all this, Esses recognizes that the use of the term *danzas* to designate sophisticated dances was more constant.[162] In fact, it is possible to identify some traits that distinguish them in "Cifras selectas de guitarra." Perhaps the clearest is the extended harmonic progression characterizing "Pavanas por la E" (fol. 4v [no. 4]), "Españoletas por la E" (fol. 6r [no. 5]), and "Paradetas por la C" (fol. 22r [no. 16]), which is difficult to find in most of the *bailes* (example 11).[163] Another kind of complexity can be seen in "El torneo por la C" (fol. 29v [no. 36]), a piece composed of several parts: a first section in duple meter, the "Batallas" (Battles) in triple meter, and two "Reverencias" (Reverences) in duple meter that take up again the last measures of the initial section. At the end, Murcia extends the piece by the addition of two brief dances, "Jácaras del torneo" (fol. 30v) and "Gallardas del torneo" (fol. 31r). The *torneo* was an old aristocratic dance that imitated the military tournaments frequently performed in secular *fiestas* in Spain, replacing lances with sticks.[164] Both in this *danza* and others cited before, the extended structure was related to the complexity of the choreography, as the *danzas* were a symbol of distinction, a refined art demanding certain knowledge and conscious training.

On the other hand, many secular songs (*tonos* or *tonadas*) from the seventeenth and early eighteenth centuries were composed on the basis of a dance type. The term *jácara*, for instance, was used with reference to both a poetic composition, usually sung, and the popular dance derived from it.[165] In the "Libro de tonos humanos," a well-known anthology from 1656, the second section of an extended song is designated as a "jácara."[166] Likewise, a vocal setting of the *villano* is found in "Romances y letras a tres voces," an earlier anthology (ca. 1610) also preserved in Madrid.[167] However, the utilization of a harmonic progression from a dance does not necessarily imply that a song was actually danced to:[168] many extant *tonos* or *tonadas* from the seventeenth century were composed to be heard in the chamber of the king, in a more contemplative attitude.[169] Hence the designation of those secular songs as dances, in the strict sense of the word, can be debatable in some cases. This raises an important point regarding Murcia's *danzas* and *bailes*, since they actually appear as instrumental pieces to be performed by guitar lovers, but not necessarily to be danced to, given that the prologue of "Cifras selectas" does not show any concern about the performance context but only provides indications for a clean execution on the

Example 11. Harmonic progression of "Pavanas por la E" (fols. 4v–6r [no. 4]).

guitar. Moreover, Minguet himself says in *Reglas y advertencias generales* that, with the purpose of learning the instrument, he bought a book written by Santiago de Murcia (*Resumen de acompañar*) from which he "also learned different curious toccatas"—i.e., instrumental pieces.[170] Perhaps a way of solving the problem lies in the topic theory and its distinction between musical types and tokens, according to which a type is "a conceptual category, a class whose reality is cognitive," while a token is an instance of that class with "a perceptual ontology."[171] From this viewpoint the *mariona*, for example, could be interpreted as a wide musical type giving rise to several specific tokens: a dance, a song for the stage, and an instrumental piece (Murcia's music falls into the latter). That is not to say that the term "dance" for referring to the pieces included in "Cifras selectas de guitarra" should be rejected, but only that one ought to be aware of their specific function.

Of course, a piece initially conceived for a specific context could also be applied to a different one. This frequently occurred with the music performed in the theater, probably the most popular entertainment of that time. It was common that a well-known song or dance was recycled to be included in a new theatrical work, while many pieces primarily composed for a specific play later acquired a great popularity and circulated independently. The *jácaras*, for instance, were frequently used during the intermissions of comedies, especially from 1630 onwards.[172] In "Cifras selectas de guitarra," perhaps the most significant example of this transfer is "La Azucena por la E" (fol. 31v [no. 37]), an elegant piece not included in Murcia's other sources. This piece was sung, with some variants, in the *Sarao de la minué francés*, an undated theatrical work by Juan Francisco Tejera. The music of this brief play is preserved in the Valladolid cathedral and has been edited by Carmelo Caballero. It includes three *tonadas*, the third of which is "La Azucena es bella y fina."[173] Caballero argues that it probably was a preexisting piece included by Tejera in his own work, since it appears in the "Libro de tonos puestos en cifra de arpa" and other literary sources as an independent song.[174] This hypothesis is strengthened by the appearance of a piece entitled "La Azucena, o minuet" in Sebastián de Aguirre's manuscript (fol. 3r) for zither and guitar, preserved in Mexico (Saldívar collection) and apparently copied in the late seventeenth century.[175] It is also possible that the piece was created for the stage and popularized afterward, although the fact that both Tejera's work and the concordant musical sources are undated makes it difficult to go further in this conjecture. On the other hand, the harp version is quite close to the theatrical one as represented in the Valladolid source; for example, both include a G-sharp in the third measure in an authentic cadence to V, while Murcia's setting uses a G-natural in a cadence iv^6–V.

The case of "La Azucena" confirms in a general sense Russell's intuition about a possible link between Murcia's pieces and the Spanish stage from the beginning of the eighteenth century.[176] Nevertheless, can it be said that Murcia directly collaborated with Tejera or other authors by composing or performing theatrical songs, or rather that he arranged some well-known pieces for the guitar that originated from the theater? While there is no certain response at this moment, it is clear that detailed research in the field of Madrilenian theater around 1700 is a necessary step in Murcia studies, which might fill the current gap in his life between his marriage in 1695 and his entrance to the court in 1704.

Most of the Spanish genres mentioned so far were cultivated in Hispanic America, as proven by the Mexican sources quoted in the first section. Sebastián de Aguirre's manuscript also includes, among other dances, *pavanas*, *gallardas*, *vacas*, *marionas*, and *jácaras*.[177] Moreover, some of the main features characterizing Spanish dances and *tonos*, especially from the seventeenth century, such as the predominance of triple meter and the *hemiola* or wavering between $\frac{3}{2}$ and $\frac{3}{1}$ measures (currently transcribed as $\frac{6}{8}$ and $\frac{3}{4}$), can be found in many traditional dances from different regions of Latin America, such as the Peruvian *marinera*, the Mexican *son*, the *bambuco* in Colombia and Venezuela, and the *cueca* in Bolivia and Chile.[178] Nevertheless, the great scarcity of information for this last country about the specific dances performed during the colonial period hinders us from going further in drawing a connection between the repertory included in "Cifras selectas" and the Chilean dances from the eighteenth century.[179]

Regarding the single dances in French style, the first musical subsection of the manuscript includes seventeen minuets in different keys. This represents a notable coincidence, since "Códice Saldívar" also includes this number of minuets, a fact that might denote a standardized organization of the music genres in Murcia's personal archive, possibly related to commercial purposes. The easy, but elegant minuet (*menuet*, *minueto*) reached its great popularity from 1650 onwards. It was highly cultivated both in Spain and Hispanic America at least until the beginning of the nineteenth century,[180] as well as in Chile, where it survived even after the arrival of the republic in 1810.[181] Its great popularity is demonstrated by its preservation in the Archivo Catedralicio de Santiago, where secular dances are extremely rare.[182] It is likely that some minuets gathered by Murcia in "Cifras selectas" were conceived to be performed in pairs, as frequently occurred in the baroque (for instance, see fols. 27v [nos. 29 and 30] and 28v [nos. 33 and 34]), but I have transcribed them as separate pieces, leaving this decision to the performer. Regarding other single French dances, there is also a "Canción" (Song, fol. 39v [no. 44]) written in the style of a minuet, and a "Paspied nuevo" (fol. [42v] [no. 49]) taken from Feuillet's anthologies and previously included in Murcia's *Resumen de acompañar*,[183] apart from a *burée* and two gavottes to be commented on later.

The first subsection also includes four marches (to be discussed below), two *pasacalles*, and a suite in four movements ("Obra por la C," fol. 35v [no. 41]). The *pasacalle* (passacaglia) was not a dance but rather an instrumental piece that frequently served as an introduction for any dance or song in the same meter and key. It appeared in Spain at least in the early seventeenth century, since both Luis de Briceño and Joan Carlos Amat included *pasacalles* in their guitar books (the latter designated it as *paseo*). Its basic harmonic progression was I–IV–V–I, a structure that Murcia roughly follows, though adding new chords and usually modulating to IV between the first and second measures, perhaps to emphasize its important role in this genre. However, unlike the French "passacaille," which is a relatively brief composition commonly embedded in a suite, Murcia adheres to its Spanish and Italian counterpart by writing more extended pieces, frequently giving rise to a feeling of growth in intensity and virtuosity, as explained above.[184] On the other hand, both Russell and Pennington have noted the use of an alternative progression in some *pasacalles*: the descending tetrachord. Russell has pointed out its importance in "Pasacalles de compasillo por la E" (fol. 18v [no. 12]) as it is found in the version of "Passacalles y obras de guitarra" (fol. 23v).[185] Nevertheless, this structure represents a transformation of the main harmonic progression rather than a new framework, since it does not correspond to i–VII–VI–V, but to i–v^6–IV^6–V, as can be seen in the second variation of the *pasacalle* "A proporción por este tono" (no. 13) in the same key (example 12). In this manner, degree IV does not disappear but keeps its status within the genre.

The "Obra por la C" (fol. 35v [no. 41]) is made up of the four "classic" movements: allemande, courante, sarabande, and gigue. The first of these uses dotted rhythms to indicate the inequality, something quite frequent in most sources of composers outside France.[186] The predominant texture in this suite is homophony, occasionally interrupted by brief dialogues between the bass and the upper voice (e.g., "Correnta," mm. 32–34; "Giga," mm. 1–5). The simplicity of the suite (except for the "Correnta") is made up for by the expressive melodies and idiomatic writing, giving rise to an attractive piece. The whole, nevertheless, gives the impression of independent movements, not unified by any feature other than their overarching harmonic structure in which I–V–vi–I constitute the tonal centers (a commonplace in the suite movements in major mode at that time). This absence of unity, though not rare in baroque suites, might indicate that the piece is comprised of preexisting dances taken from different suites or sources. In fact, the "Giga" is also found in the "Coimbra Codex," a Portuguese manuscript preserved in the Biblioteca Geral da Universidade

Example 12. Second variation in *pasacalle* "A proporción por este tono" (fol. 19v [no. 13, mm. 4–8]; fol. 25v in "Passacalles y obras").

de Coimbra (M. M. 97). This source is undated and was copied by one "Joseph Carneyro Tavares Lamacense," probably in the late seventeenth century. A transcription of the piece can be found in Rogério Budasz's dissertation.[187] In addition, another setting of the "Zarabanda" is preserved in the "Libro de diferentes cifras de guitara" (1705) with the title of "Zarabanda francesa" (p. 35), albeit without attribution. Murcia's custom of assembling borrowed materials from other authors is well known (we will see this in speaking of the concordances) and it seems likely that most of the suite movements from his sources for which no concordance has as yet been identified belong to other composers as well. For instance, Hall has shown that a prelude to a suite in "Passacalles y obras" (fol. 75r), initially considered by Russell as an "original composition" of Murcia, is attributed to Corbetta in a manuscript copied by Jean-Baptiste de Castillion at the beginning of the eighteenth century, now preserved in the library of the Conservatoire Royal de Musique in Liège (Ms. 245).[188] Therefore, it is possible that the entire suite was also borrowed from other composers. Of course, that is very different from denying the possibility that some of the suite movements included in Murcia's sources are by him, as Hall does.[189] On the other hand, whether the "Zarabanda" was written by Murcia or not, there is nothing in this that weakens the hypothesis raised in the first section of this introduction that other pieces included in the "Libro de diferentes cifras," such as the *pasacalle* "por 2o. tono," indeed belong to him, since, unlike the suite movements, the concordances with Murcia's *pasacalles* are extremely rare and no one attributes them to another author.[190] At the most, they show that Murcia frequently inserts brief fragments by other composers in his *pasacalles*, as we shall see below.

As noted previously, the content of the second musical subsection of the manuscript is much more homogeneous. Apart from a *burée* and two suites, to be commented on below,[191] it gathers fifteen *pasacalles* in the main keys of the *alfabeto* system (except for F and I) grouped into pairs: a *pasacalle* in duple meter is followed by another in triple meter in the same key, the exception being "Pasacalles aclarinados por la C a compasillo" (fol. 64v [no. 66]), which is only in duple meter. Murcia follows Guerau's procedure here, the purpose of which was to provide the performer with *pasacalles* in different keys in order to introduce any dance or song. However, in "Cifras selectas," the *pasacalles* are not sequentially ordered, since the first is written "por la O," the second "por el +," the third "por la B," etc.

Given that the main features of this genre, as well as Murcia's mastery of it, have been commented on above, I would like to end this section with a further reflection on another subject: the implications of the manuscript's structure described so far. The division of "Cifras selectas" into two musical subsections, one with a heterogeneous content (Spanish and French dances, one suite, marches, etc.) and the other mainly composed of *pasacalles* and "obras" (two extant suites plus three lost ones included in the last fifteen folios), presents a clear parallelism with the previously known manuscripts by Murcia, "Códice Saldívar no. 4" and "Passacalles y obras de guitarra." This statement is confirmed by a study of concordances of the manuscript to be detailed later: all the concordances with "Códice Saldívar" are included in the first subsection, while all but three of the concordances with "Passacalles y obras" are included in the second. The correspondence is even more striking if we consider that the two subsections may have originally been two independent manuscripts, as explained in the description of the source. Far from being insignificant, this fact reveals a careful organization of musical genres by Murcia, as does the coincidence between the number of minuets in "Cifras selectas" and "Códice Saldívar." It seems that he divided his music into two major categories, something that was not new at that time. The "Libro de tonos puestos en cifra de arpa," for instance, states in its list of contents: "This book does not include *pasacalles* nor instrumental pieces, because they are included in another book; and this one only contains songs" (no tiene este libro pasacalles, ni tañidos, porque de ellos hay libro aparte; y éste solo es de tonos).[192] All of this not only highlights once again the apparent character of the manuscript as a commercial source, but also reveals a sort of production strategy in keeping with such a character. Apparently, the guitarist was prepared to satisfy specific demands by the guitar lovers of his time. Finally, noting the similarity between "Cifras selectas de guitarra," on the one hand, and both "Códice Saldívar" and "Pasacalles y obras" when put together, on the other, strengthens to some extent Lorimer's argument that the latter indeed were conceived—or presented—as two volumes of a single anthology, in spite of the doubts set out about this in the first part of this introduction.

Music and Society

In the previous sections, the relationship between the music of "Cifras selectas de guitarra" and the environment in which it was produced has already been approached in different manners, since, in a way, historical, biographical, and social conditions represent important keys to understanding music. My purpose here is to invert this order by accessing historical and social aspects through an examination of some pieces gathered in the manuscript, on the belief that music not only reflects society and culture, but also "contributes to their formation and may lead to discoveries about them [that] are not otherwise available,"[193] something that, as we shall see, even affects Murcia's biography. And while this approach is neither hermeneutic nor semiotic in the strict sense, it deals with meaning in music as historically grounded.[194]

The first point concerns Spanish dances in general. Since most of them were defined to a large extent by a harmonic progression, solely by hearing that progression a competent listener—that is to say, one who held a minimal appreciation and knowledge of music—could identify the dance in question at that time, just as one can today. However, given that the taxonomy of dances in the seventeenth and early eighteenth centuries usually divided them into *danzas* and *bailes,* as explained above, it is patently obvious that such identification bore images and ideas with social connotations—a *pavana*, indeed, was not only a dance but an aristocratic dance. While this assertion is not very informative, given the vagueness of a label such as "aristocratic dance," it allows us to wonder how much more specific structural devices in "Cifras selectas" succeeded in connecting the music to its context.

The "Jácaras francesas por la D" (fol. 8v [no. 7]) is an appropriate example. This genre appears to be of recent invention, since apart from Murcia's "Cifras selectas" and "Códice Saldívar" (fol. 29r), the only source preserving it is the "Libro de diferentes cifras" copied in 1705.[195] Musically, these French *jácaras* begin with virtually the same harmonic progression as the traditional "Jácaras por la E" (fol. 1r [no. 1]), but include a second phrase where this progression is transposed up a fifth (example 13), which represents their only distinctive trait. It is clear that this gesture parodies the modulation to the fifth (or third) degree at the end of the first part so common in French binary dances,[196] but mostly alien to Spanish ones, with their structure of theme and variations fitting a single mode. Thus, in the field of Spanish dance of the early eighteenth century, the modulation to the fifth degree can be interpreted as a *topic* of Frenchness.[197]

Two other pieces supply new elements for this reflection: the "Villanos por la C" (fol. 20v [no. 14]) and "Caballero por la C" (fol. 21r [no. 15]). While the first, in principle, was an antique *baile* and the second a more refined *danza*, they are placed consecutively both in "Cifras selectas" and "Códice Saldívar" (fols. 7r and 8r), and present a parallelism in their musical features, sharing even some melodic lines.[198] Their harmonic progressions are indeed the same, except for the fact that the "Caballero" presents an additional phrase with a brief excursion to the fifth degree (example 14). To understand this sort of rhetorical gesture,[199] we have to consider the different meanings that the word *caballero* (gentleman) held at the beginning of the eighteenth century. Although it originally designated men of nobility of antique origin, it seems to have lost some of its prestige as more and more people began to claim an old lineage in order to ascend in the social sphere, something possibly related to the increasing power of a budding bourgeoisie. Indeed, in 1729 the dictionary of the *Real Academia Española* includes the concept of "getting into *caballero*," defining it as "pretending to be more than one is: which is commonly said of many people who, having acquired some money and seeking to increase their fortune, start to deal with well-known men to show off among their equals."[200] At the same time, from the second half of the seventeenth century on the character of a *caballero* was presented as decrepit and dressed in ridiculous cos-

Example 13. Harmonic progressions in "Jácaras por la E" (fols. 1r–2r [no. 1]) and "Jácaras francesas por la D" (fols. 8v–9v [no. 7]).

tumes,[201] while the word *villano* was partly associated with someone rustic, discourteous, and even mean.[202] Consequently, the "character" in "Cifras selectas," as well as in "Códice Saldívar," is not an authentic *caballero*, but rather a *villano* disguised as one, which explains its appearance as a *baile* in table 1. And the only mask hindering us from discovering him is the excursion to the fifth degree in the second part of the harmonic progression of the piece. A confirmation of this statement can be found in the "Libro de diferentes cifras," which, once again, presents a notable parallelism with Murcia's sources: there the two equivalent pieces are called, respectively, "Villano" and "Villano caballero" (p. 104).[203] Therefore, the excursion to the fifth degree functions as a topic for elegance and gentility, and putting it together with the similar one in "Jácaras francesas" (no. 7) we become aware of the fact that around 1700 in Madrid, gentility and Frenchness were two closely related concepts. There is nothing new in this: the French cultural influence in Spain about 1700 is a well-known fact that has partly been dealt with in this introduction,[204] but the interest here consists in ascertaining its implications for the music itself.

The mixture of different styles and genres reflects another feature proper to Madrid at that time: the juncture of local and foreign (French, Italian) traditions. In the musical sphere, this gave rise to somewhat hybrid genres, such as the so-called *operatic zarzuela,* which mixed traditional *coplas* and *seguidillas* with the recitative and the da capo aria,[205] or the sacred *villancico*, traditionally composed of an *estribillo* and alternated *coplas*, which increasingly included recitatives and arias after about 1700, and especially after Philip V's marriage to Isabel de Farnesio, whose predilection for Italian music is well known.[206] These contextual factors can help us to understand a group of pieces included in both "Cifras selectas" (fol. 45r and following [no. 53]) and "Passacalles y obras" (fol. 58r and following), though with considerable variants. These pieces are titled "Idea nueva de clarines primorosos por la C" (fol. 45r), "Canción airosa" (fol. 46r), "Llamadas" (fol. 46r), "Marcha" (fol. 47r), "Canción de ecos" (fol. 48r), "Fajina" (fol. 48r), and "Idea de dos clarines" (fol. 48v). Its independence is corroborated both by its position at the beginning of the second musical subsection of the manuscript and the suite in another key following the "Idea de dos clarines." Nonetheless, it does not correspond to a miscellaneous composition,[207] as

Example 14. Harmonic progressions in "Villanos por la C" (fols. 20v–21r [no. 14]) and "Caballero por la C" (fols. 21r–21v [no. 15]).

proven by the overall title supplied in the list of contents of "Cifras selectas": "Idea nueva, y obra especial de clarines" (New idea, and special suite [in the style] of trumpets).[208] This title is entirely analogous to one in the list of contents of "Passacalles y obras": "Preludio por la E y obra" (Prelude in the E and suite). Thus this group of pieces is merely a suite, of which the first movement—"Idea nueva de clarines primorosos por la C"—represents the prelude.[209] This function is confirmed by its improvisatory character, with rapid scales and arpeggios, combined with proper features of music in the *clarines* style, such as repetitions of notes and a thin texture.[210] Although this style is not specifically Spanish, since it corresponds to the genre of battle music cultivated in other parts of Europe, Russell has proven that at least four pieces of Murcia's suite coincide with different battle pieces included in the well-known organ manuscript by Antonio Martín y Coll, "Flores de música," copied at the beginning of the eighteenth century.[211] Hence, the hybridization here consists of integrating a Spanish repertory in the foreign structure of the suite, which explains the adjective of "special" or "particular" used by Murcia. But the structural analogies with the suite do not stop there: the brief "Fajina" is placed both in "Cifras selectas" and "Passacalles y obras" close to the end of the suite, before the last piece. Given that the "Fajina" was written in $\frac{12}{8}$, it could be interpreted as an allusion to the gigue, and more precisely to the Italian gigue that Murcia gathers in his transcriptions of Corelli's work. This interpretation is all the more feasible as the *fajina* is defined by the *Real Academia Española* as a military call, ordering the troops to retreat.[212] On the other hand, it is worth noting that both the first ("Idea nueva . . .") and the last ("Idea de dos clarines") pieces of the suite in "Cifras selectas" were fused by Murcia in "Passacalles y obras" in order to make up a single and more extended piece, a fact proving the inadequacy of the concept of "work" when applied to much of the repertory that he gathered and composed, which is rather similar to a written improvisation, as explained in the previous section.

If the cases examined so far point to broad aspects of Madrid's culture at the beginning of the eighteenth century, three of the four marches included in the first subsection of the manuscript might be related to more concrete events, even casting some light on obscure facets of Murcia's life. The first is the "Marcha valona" (fol. 40r [no. 46]) (Walloon march), a somewhat baffling piece because of its similitude to a dance in binary form instead of a march in an archetypal sense. The abovementioned manuscript by Sebastián de Aguirre, indeed, includes four pieces entitled "Valona de bailar" (for dancing), although the other three are indicated as "Valona de glosar," i.e., for improvisation or variation.[213] Be that as it may, it seems that the "Marcha valona" was inspired by the *guardia valona* (Walloon guard), a special military corps created by Philip V in 1702–3,[214] when Murcia in all likelihood was active in Madrid. Yet another piece that could have been inspired by a military corps is the "Marcha de los carabineros" (fol. 40v [no. 47]), possibly linked with the companies of *carabineros* (soldiers on horseback with carbines) present in Madrid in the early eighteenth century, or with the foundation of the brigade of "Carabineros Reales" which brought all of them together.[215] The information I have been able to find about the date in which this foundation took place is confusing, since, while most authors place it in 1730, at least one text indicates it was in 1705.[216] If the latter were true, the appearance of a similar "Marcha de carabineros" in the "Libro de diferentes cifras" (p. 130), copied just in that year, would confirm such a link. But at any rate these pieces depict in one way or another the environment in which Murcia was active and gathered his guitar anthologies.

Of even more interest is the incomplete "Marcha de las guardias de la Reina Ana" (fol. 41v [no. 48]) (March of Queen Ann's Guards),[217] because of its allusion to a specific personage. There are at least two likely candidates to whom this march could refer: Anne Stuart, queen of England from 1702 to 1714, and Maria Anna of Neuburg, the second wife of Charles II, queen consort of Spain from 1690 to 1700.[218] But, whoever it was, the interesting thing is that Murcia hints at someone who was on the side opposed to Philip V and the Bourbon dynasty. During the War of Spanish Succession, England and the Grand Alliance declared war on Spain and France, supporting Archduke Charles of Austria in his attempt to reach the throne of Spain. Maria Anna of Neuburg, in turn, did her best to convince Charles II to grant the throne to the archduke, and when the troops of the latter entered Madrid in June 1706 she did not take long in declaring her submission to him as the new king of Spain; later, Philip V, in retaliation for this attitude, deported her to Bayonne.[219] This piece of information is significant because, as explained in the first section, Murcia did not go with Marie Louise of Savoy to Burgos in June 1706, unlike other musicians who worked in the queen's household. The organist Diego Jaraba, who remained in Madrid as well, was suspected of betrayal, and while there is no information concerning Murcia on that subject, we have seen that in 1708, when he requested payment for the first semester of 1706, the queen ordered to proceed with him exactly "as done with his partner Mr. Diego Jaraba." Although the latter denied any fidelity to the Hapsburg dynasty, the portraits of Philip IV, Marie Louise of Orleans (Charles II's first wife), and John of Austria the younger (Charles II's half-brother) recently found by Morales in his inventory, as well as the absence of any

xxix

portrait of Philip V, give him away.[220] That is why this march is so significant: in the absence of paintings, it nevertheless seems to suggest Murcia's adherence to a figure unfriendly to the Bourbons.

Notwithstanding, the clues might not stop there since there seems to be another personage from the Hapsburg period represented in "Cifras selectas," although to unveil her we have to go back in time to 1679, when Murcia was about six years old. In November of that year, Charles II married Marie Louise of Orleans, a French noblewoman of the Bourbon dynasty. A few months later, on 3 March 1680, Pedro Calderón de la Barca presented his last play, *Hado y Divisa*, in which, impressed by the pale beauty of the new queen, he represented, and, in a manner of speaking, baptized her as an "azucena" (white lily).[221] The metaphor was widely adopted given that some years later, in Madrid, the people recited a stanza in which the queen was called "beautiful lily."[222] Hence, in all likelihood the abovementioned "La Azucena por la E" (fol. 31v [no. 37]), a piece already included in Sebastián de Aguirre's manuscript from the late seventeenth century, represented Marie Louise of Orleans. If true, Murcia does not hint at one, but at two personages connected to the Hapsburg empire, in contrast to an absence of references to figures representative of Philip V's era in his manuscript. This suggested inclination of Murcia toward the Hapsburg dynasty would result in a new interpretation for his apparent absence from the court after 1706, as well as for his allusions to his adverse luck in both *Resumen de acompañar* and "Códice Saldívar." Thus, we should admit that a careful observation of the pieces included in "Cifras selectas de guitarra" can contribute new perspectives for our understanding of Murcia and his world.

An Intertextual Music: Concordances, Recomposition, and Quotations

In a wide sense, any music—actually any text—can be considered as intertextual in the sphere of genre and style, as it incorporates in one way or another references to stylistic patterns, conventions, procedures, and discourses, that is, to other "texts" outside itself.[223] Though admitting to the validity of such a statement, for the purposes of this introduction I will focus on intertextual relations in the narrower—and perhaps more practical—level of strategies,[224] exploring thus specific and concrete links between the music of "Cifras selectas de guitarra" and other sources. For instance, I have not considered those pieces having only harmonic similarities as significantly concordant, given that, as in the case of Spanish dances, a harmonic progression in common does not imply a special link. Hence the fact that some pieces, such as "Pavanas por la E" (no. 4), "Paradetas por la C" (no. 16), and "Marcha de los carabineros" (no. 47) are indicated as not having any concordance implies that, according to my criteria, the extant version in "Cifras selectas" does not present a significant resemblance to the alternative versions of the same genre found in other sources. Of course, some cases may be debatable, in spite of the accuracy I have tried to ensure in this task. In any event, the significant concordances identified so far, undoubtedly to be expanded by future researches, are summarized in table 2 (see the appendix to this introduction).[225]

In the category of *diferencias*—i.e., Spanish dances and *pasacalles*—a concordance indicates that two pieces have variations in common, but it should not be confused with an identity between them. As their flexible structure offers different options to the composer (addition or suppression of variations, changes in their order, etc.), in most cases they are very different, as we shall see below. So different that a concordant piece might even be of greater interest than an "original" or unique one, both for the performer and the scholar.

In spite of this, let us begin by considering those pieces that are almost identical to ones in a concordant source belonging to another composer. First of all, although the influence of François Campion seems not to have been as important in "Cifras selectas" as in "Passacalles y obras," all the movements of the "Obra por la K3" (fol. 50v [no. 54]) are also found in his *Nouvelles découvertes sur la guitarre*, published in Paris in 1705. The "Preludio por la K3," "Alemanda," and "Giga" were taken from a brief suite in three movements, and the "Correnta" and "Zarabanda" were extracted from another suite placed later in Campion's book.[226] Murcia transposed the first three of these pieces a step down in order to fit them with the other two, pitched in C. Apart from this, and although in the original source the pieces were written in particular tunings or *scordature*, Murcia did not introduce significant changes. Some passages might have been modified because of the stringing that he used. For example, while the entry of the second voice in the version of the gigue by Campion is in an octave d + d', both notes being played on different courses, Murcia only indicates a c' in the third course (example 15), perhaps because the fifth course of his instrument did not have a bourdon (lower string). Nevertheless, the appropriate tuning for Murcia's music is still a matter of discussion.

It is also a well-known fact that several pieces gathered by Murcia in "Passacalles y obras" are found as well in the manuscript Ms.s. 5615 of the Conservatoire Royale de Musique in Brussels ("Recueil des pièces de guitarre"), copied by the Flemish clergyman Jean Baptiste de Castillion in 1730, the first section of which includes music by the Belgian composer François Le Cocq.[227] Once again, the influence of this composer is much less important in "Cifras selectas": only the incomplete second "Gavota" of folio 43v (no. 52) corresponds to an "Air" included in the Castillion manuscript.[228]

Yet Murcia might have extracted pieces from the work of another composer, the Franciscan Antonio Martín y Coll, active in Madrid in the first half of the eighteenth century. As explained in the previous section, Russell has shown how most of the pieces composing the "Idea nueva, y obra especial de clarines" (fol. 45r [no. 53]) are concordant with the first of Martín y Coll's "Flores de música," four organ manuscripts that he gathered from roughly 1706 to 1709. Nonetheless, it is not clear at all how many of the pieces collected by Martín y Coll are indeed by him, given that, in spite of the scarcity of attri-

Example 15. Beginning of the "Giga" in *Nouvelles découvertes* (p. 51) and "Cifras selectas" (fol. 52r [no. 54]).

butions, it has been possible to determine that several of them belong to other composers, such as Aguilera de Heredia, Cabanilles, Antonio de Cabezón, and Frescobaldi.[229] Hence the "Canción de ecos" and "Fajina" may correspond to transcriptions of well-known pieces or melodies in contemporary Madrid, instead of original compositions by either Martín y Coll or Murcia.

Likewise, it is not clear at all how Murcia was able to know Le Cocq's work when the latter apparently never printed it. There are many alternatives, since the Low Countries and Spain were well connected at that time. Hall suggested in her dissertation that Murcia could have had access to his work by having visited the Netherlands, especially considering that his *Resumen* was in all likelihood printed in Antwerp.[230] We should also not forget that the French composer Henry Desmarest was in Brussels in about 1699–1701, before arriving in Madrid. His purpose was apparently to enter the court of the elector of Bavaria, Maximilian Emanuel, who resided there between 1693 and 1701.[231] According to Castillion, Le Cocq had taught guitar to the elector's wife,[232] so it seems likely that Desmarest had access to Le Cocq's music during his sojourn there, and he certainly had several occasions to be in contact with Murcia between 1701 and 1706, when he served as music master of Philip V's chamber. But, at such a conjectural level, I think there are also other possibilities to be considered, although nobody seems willing to accept them: that Le Cocq borrowed some of Murcia's pieces;[233] that the borrowing was reciprocal; or that both guitarists borrowed some pieces from other sources. After all, nothing is known about Le Cocq other than the indirect information supplied by Castillion in his preface. Additionally, the latter was acquainted with Spanish guitar music of the seventeenth century, since he stated in the prologue that his father had studied guitar in Madrid around 1690—the date, of course, is approximate—with Miguel Pérez de Zavala, whose work he partly gathered in the second section of the "Recueil." Hall has expressed her disagreement with all this, arguing that Castillion explicitly states that Le Cocq gave him autographed copies of his pieces.[234] Castillion, indeed, is clear in entitling the first section of his manuscript as "Recueil des pièces de guitarre *composées* para Mr. François Le Cocq" (my italics). Notwithstanding, this statement is false, or at least not completely true, given that the minuet on page 63 appears in Robert de Visée's second book for guitar published in Paris in 1686.[235] The case is all the more complex if one considers that the passage of music and musicians between Spain and the rest or Europe was a circular process, in spite of the precedence that France held at that time. Desmarets, indeed, went back temporarily to Flanders in March 1704, before leaving Madrid for good.[236] Of course, with these reflections it is not my intention to deny that Murcia possibly borrowed music by Le Cocq, which seems likely taking into account the numerous pieces by other composers that he included in "Passacalles y obras," as Hall and Russell have shown, but only to cast some prudent doubt on a still little-known process, as the circulation of guitar music in the early eighteenth century in fact is.

Be that as it may, what is clear is that the pieces of the "Obra por la K3" (no. 54) are indeed by Campion and were borrowed by Murcia from the *Nouvelles découvertes sur la guitarre*. The prelude, allemande, and gigue were even copied from consecutive pages of this edition, as well as the courante and sarabande. The fact that Murcia did not indicate the name of Campion, as he did in his transcriptions of Corelli's work, is striking, however. On the one hand, the practice of making up a suite with borrowed movements, or introducing minimal changes in a preexistent work without indicating its original composer, was a common one in the seventeenth and eighteenth centuries. The concept of intellectual property was far less developed than today and, to a large extent, the concept of composition itself was still conceived as a process of rearrangement of previous materials.[237] Nevertheless, as contradictory as it may seem, at the same time contemporary composers were not unaware of the value of their own work, and not indifferent to unauthorized borrowing by other musicians. For instance, Corbetta and Granata accused each other of plagiarism in the second half of the seventeenth century.[238] It is also possible that the connotations of borrowing a piece in a manuscript of more private circulation were different from those of including it in a printed edition, with its wider circulation, official character, and greater profits. Yet Murcia might not have tried to attribute the borrowed pieces to himself, since neither in "Cifras selectas" nor in "Passacalles y obras" does the title explicitly indicate that he composed the pieces, as in Le Cocq's "Recueil" by Castillion.[239] On the other hand, the fact that he explicitly attributed some pieces to Corelli might be explained by a wish to highlight the attractiveness of his own sources through the inclusion of a well-known composer. In any case, the problem is more complex than it may seem at first glance.

Another important source in the domain of concordances, this time anonymous, is the "Libro de diferentes cifras," copied in 1705 and preserved in the Biblioteca Nacional de Madrid, the importance of which has been dealt with in previous sections. As can be seen in table 2 of the appendix, two minuets (fols. 24v and 25r [nos. 18 and 20]), the "Zarabanda" of the "Obra por la C" (fol. 36v [no. 41]), and the *passacalle* "A proporción" (fol. 54r [no. 57]) appear in that source with minor variants. Besides these, an entire variation of "Gallardas del torneo" (fol. 31r of "El torneo por la C" [no. 36]) is virtually identical to one in the version of the "Libro." While the authorship of the minuets, the "Zarabanda," and the "Gallardas" may be put into question, in all likelihood the *pasacalle* was written by Murcia himself, since no other concordance has been found either for it or for the rest of the *pasacalles* included in his sources. In addition, the "Marcha de los oboes" (fol. 40r [no. 45]) is also found in the "Libro de diferentes cifras," but with the title of "Aboe." Unlike the version in "Cifras selectas," the main melody has been charged to the fourth and fifth courses. And, apart from the concordant pieces in the strict sense, the "Libro de diferentes cifras" also includes several dance types that have only been found in Murcia's sources, such as the "Jácaras francesas" (no. 7) and "El Amor" (no. 8). Besides, there is a striking similitude between the strummed introductions of the "Paracumbé" included in the "Libro" and the "Cumbé" of "Códice Saldívar," as explained in the first section (see example 2), and although these particular chords might correspond to a typical way of starting this kind of dance, as far as I know they have not been found in other sources. Thus in my opinion, taken as a whole, these links constitute sufficient evidence to suggest that the copyist of the "Libro" gathered some pieces by Murcia, since that source was an anthology of pieces by well-known guitarists from that time, as he was about 1705. If true, some of the concordant pieces, if not all, may be earlier versions of those to be gathered later in "Cifras selectas," "Códice Saldívar," and "Passacalles y obras."

Despite the importance of "Libro de diferentes cifras" and the books by Campion and Castillion (copying the music of Le Cocq), most of the concordances for "Cifras selectas de guitarra" have been found in Murcia's own sources. While only four pieces concord with *Resumen de acompañar*,[240] I have found nineteen concordances with "Códice Saldívar" and twenty-five with "Passacalles y obras." As for the "Códice," all the concordant pieces are dance types, while, as regards the latter, fifteen concordances are *pasacalles*. As explained above, all those pieces are written in the flexible structure of *diferencias,* so that the concordant versions present important variants from those in "Cifras selectas," giving rise in many cases to very different pieces. For example, of the sixteen variations comprising "Jácaras por la E" (fol. 1r [no. 1]), Murcia uses only four in "Códice Saldívar," changing their order; and of the twenty variations contained in "Marionas por la B" (fol. 2r [no. 2]) in "Cifras selectas," the version of "Códice Saldívar" uses only five.[241] In the "Españoletas por la E" (fol. 6r [no. 5]), in turn, the harmonic progression in the version of "Códice Saldívar" has been modified: Murcia shortened it by suppressing the last eight measures. In addition, in most of the versions in "Códice Saldívar," Murcia includes a strummed introduction presenting the harmonic progression characteristic of each dance type. On the other hand, pieces such as "Difrencias de gallardas por la E" (no. 3), "Folías españolas por la E" (no. 6), and, moreover, "Jácaras francesas por la D" (no. 7) present more subtle differences.

As these pieces appear as alternative versions of a somewhat abstract harmonic progression (i.e., legitimate tokens of the same type), the term "recomposition," implying the deliberate modification of a previous and fixed text, is debatable when applied to them. On the contrary, a clear example of recomposition is found in the "Burée" of folio 52v (no. 55), which is undoubtedly linked to a "Rigodon" attributed to François Le Cocq in the "Recueil des pièces de guitarre" (p. 53) copied by Castillion. Taking for granted the likely alternative that it was Murcia who reused Le Cocq's piece, his task consisted of dividing the "Rigodon" into smaller units (modules, as Russell calls them), which he reordered freely, adding new fragments in order to ensure a logical sequence. For example, the beginning of the "Burée" is taken from the second part of the "Rigodon" (see example 16). This constitutes a recomposition in an archetypal sense, and the result is a new piece as interesting as the original one.

But perhaps the most interesting procedure used by Murcia consists of inserting quotations of pieces by other composers within his own compositions. Although I have found only two examples of this practice, I suspect that further research will supply new cases. Not surprisingly, both are *diferencias,* their flexible structure constituting an appropriate field for this sort of procedure. The first case is found in a *pasacalle* "A proporción" (fol. 56v [no. 59]) of "Cifras selectas," where the seventh variation is a quotation of the fifth variation of Gaspar Sanz's "Passacalles por la +."[242] The other example is the version of "Marionas por la B" included in "Códice Saldívar" (fol. 3v), where Murcia quotes two variations of a chaconne attributed to Corbetta in Castillion's "Recueil des pièces de guitarre" (pp. 106–7). The correspondence is undeniable, as can be seen in the transcription of both fragments (example 17).[243] Since the attribution to Corbetta is reliable enough and some of his pieces are indeed borrowed in "Passacalles y obras,"[244] it seems that Murcia is deliberately quoting a well-known composer, as he did with Sanz in "Cifras selectas." Given that we have interpreted his *diferencias* as a kind of written improvisation, it is possible that contemporary jazz can offer an appropriate framework to understand such a practice, in spite of the cultural and temporal distance. As everybody knows, jazz musicians usually quote and transform preexisting motives by well-known composers during their improvisations without any intention of concealing such motives to their listeners, in an attitude that has been designated as the "joy of influence," in opposition to Harold Bloom's theory about the "anxiety of influence." In doing so, they not only pay tribute to their precursors and show a great knowledge of jazz repertory, but they also involve "the audience in the process," making it "meaningful for those who recognize the sources." And while they often parody their precursors in more sophisticated ways understandable only to specialists, they also insert borrowed motives in a way that "the knowledgeable but not necessarily specialist jazz listener would be likely to understand."[245] In this manner a chain of associations is set off, engaging the listener and uniting "her or him with a community of other individuals who share a similar musical point of view."[246] There is an

Example 16. Transcription of the "Rigodon" by Le Cocq in "Recueil des pièces de guitarre" (p. 53), indicating its correspondences to the "Burée" in "Cifras selectas" (fol. 52v [no. 55]).

Example 17. Transcription of concordant passages between "Marionas por la B" in "Códice Saldívar" (fol. 3v) and a chaconne by Corbetta in "Recueil des pièces de guitarre" (p. 106).

irrefutable likeness between these features of jazz improvisation and what Murcia does in quoting Sanz and Corbetta. He, indeed, inserts the motives in an understandable manner for someone well-acquainted with the mainstream of guitar music at that time; and, while both pieces are written down in their current state, it is not daring to imagine that they reflect a common practice in "live music performances" (theater, chamber music, etc.). In one way or another, this procedure was possibly intended to attract the attention of an audience and engage it in a sort of communicative process in which a listener and the composer/performer shared their delight in identifying the borrowing, and this is valid whether it was a live audience or a potential one (the readers of Murcia's books).

Notes on Performance

Aside from the contribution of "Cifras selectas de guitarra" to the baroque guitar repertory, its great interest also lies in its prologue ("Explicación"). It is the only extended writing by Murcia known so far, apart from the introductory section of *Resumen de acompañar*, which includes the dedication to Andriani, an explanation of the *abecedario* and the suspensions, and a preface to the reader added later. But, unlike those texts, the prologue of "Cifras selectas" deals with performance issues in a more systematic way, as regards both technical and stylistic aspects.

With respect to the left hand, we have seen that Murcia uses dots to indicate the fingering. But he does so only until folio 26v, arguing this will be enough for the amateur to get used to the appropriate practice. As he declares, his purpose is to assure the comfort and order of the hand,[247] undoubtedly one of his main pedagogical concerns, since in the *Resumen de acompañar* he had already referred to it.[248] Among the practical consequences, the ascending and descending whole-steps are frequently fingered using the index and little fingers, thus avoiding a greater extension of the hand.[249] Murcia also consistently avoids having the little finger pressing the fourth or fifth courses, or a lower course than one pressed by the index finger, because that would imply a tortuous position for the left hand. In "Pasacalles de compasillo por la D," measure 27 (fol. 62v [no. 64]), I have found an exceptional case in which this occurs, if we follow the left-hand

Example 18. "Pasacalles de compasillo por la D" (fol. 62v [no. 64, mm. 25–28]). The left-hand fingering comes from "Passacalles y obras" (fol. 20v).

Example 19. Fragment of "Folías españolas por la E" in "Cifras selectas" (fol. 8r [no. 6, mm. 52–55]) and "Códice Saldívar" (fol. 22v).

fingering of "Passacalles y obras" (example 18). In general, I share Russell's conclusion that this aspect "takes precedence over voice-leading concerns and the smooth connection of contrapuntal voices."[250] That is to say, in only a few cases does Murcia use an intricate fingering to avoid cutting off a voice, and that, of course, has important implications for the transcription of his music. On the other hand, the left hand can sometimes reveal Murcia's particular articulation or phrasing,[251] allowing us to approach his own performance. For example, the left-hand fingering in "Pasacalles de compasillo por la E," measure 4 (fol. 18v [no. 12]), implies cutting off the bass in a sort of staccato, perhaps with some emphasis.

Nonetheless, there are a few arguments against considering Murcia's fingering as a dogma. First, since the manuscript—as well as *Resumen de acompañar*—is directed primarily to amateurs, we could wonder if the left-hand fingering was not also exclusively thought of for them, while Murcia, as an expert guitarist, could pay greater attention to the voice-leading in his own performances, using a fingering in keeping with that. Second, the possibility of comparing the left-hand fingering of "Cifras selectas" with concordant passages in other of Murcia's sources at times contributes to clearing up any doubt of his intention, but occasionally it also shows divergences indicating erroneous and doubtful passages. For example, in "Folías españolas por la E," measure 53 (fol. 8r [no. 6]), the fingering implies cutting off the bass voice, but the version in "Códice Saldívar" offers the alternative to sustain it (example 19). Of course, that is not an invitation to the performer to ignore Murcia's left-hand fingering, but only to consider it in a critical way when reading the tablature.

The most interesting and original parts of the prologue, however, concern the right hand. Murcia indicates that laying the little finger "near the bridge of the guitar" (fuera de la puente de la guitarra) is typical of beginners, but a skillful guitarist must play with the hand in the air, "especially when the pieces are delicate and include strummed strokes, as in these cases the instrument must be played in the middle" (mayormente cuando son obras delicadas, y en ellas hay golpes rasgueados, pues debe en estos casos tocarse en el medio del instrumento). In other words, he recommends strumming with the right hand in a position close to the junction between the neck and body of the instrument, in order to achieve a delicate sonority. In a recent edition of baroque guitar music, indeed, Frank Koonce had already defended the appropriateness of such a technique without knowing "Cifras selectas," both on the basis of practical reasons (to provide contrast in repeating sections) and iconographical evidence (baroque paintings of guitarists).[252] The coincidence between his opinion and the quoted paragraph could not be greater. In this manner, Murcia discards a technique—the laying of the little finger—that was very common in playing lute-like instruments. Notwithstanding, he accepts it when accompanying another instrument, in order to obtain greater sonority,[253] which denotes the importance of the guitar for continuo playing.

A striking idea, from a modern viewpoint, is Murcia's statement that the strings must be plucked only with "the thumb, index, and middle fingers" (el pulgar, el índice y el del corazón). The ring finger of the right hand, indeed, performed a secondary function on the Spanish baroque guitar, similar to that of the little finger on the modern instrument. Sanz, for example, accepted its use only when necessary, and Guerau did not mention it in the prologue of his *Poema harmonico*, though the pieces of this book occasionally indicate the simultaneous plucking of four courses.[254] Murcia goes a step further, since in "Cifras selectas" the plucked style is restricted to three-part chords, while four- and five-part chords are always strummed.[255] The practice is the same in the other sources by him. Only in the first section of the *Resumen de acompañar* does he indicate a few four-part chords in plucked style,[256] perhaps because the theoretical character of this section—an accompaniment treatise—implies a greater concern for voice-leading. But in the anthology of pieces in guitar tablature (second section) only the three-part chords are plucked. Thus, Murcia virtually did not use the ring finger of the right hand. This feature of his technique is related to the thin texture of his music and arrangements, as well as the frequent rupture of the voice-leading. The avoidance of four-part texture might also indicate the use of a totally re-entrant tuning (i.e., without low strings in the fourth and fifth courses), since such a limited register would render fruitless the use of four voices. Nonetheless, in the editorial policies we shall see that the problem of guitar tuning is much more complex than this.

Murcia also assigns the index and middle fingers of the right hand to the first and second courses, stating that the thumb must be used to pluck only the third, fourth, and fifth ones. This seems to be a general recommendation that cannot be taken literally, as some passages in *campanelas* would be difficult to play without plucking the third course with the index finger. All the same, some similarity with Guerau on this point might indicate that he trained Murcia, as Russell suggested.[257] Additionally, Murcia coincides with modern practice (and also with Guerau) in indicating that the index and middle fingers must pluck the strings alternately.[258]

Murcia's prologue casts light on a somewhat controversial issue: the appropriate execution of the trill in his music. Russell suggested that the main-note trill should be used in Murcia's pieces written in Spanish style (*diferencias*), while the trill beginning on the upper auxiliary note was recommended for his pieces in the French style (minuets, *contredanses*, etc.).[259] Robert Strizich, in turn, recognized the predominance of the main-note trill in Spanish music, but recommended the upper-note trill for Murcia on the basis of the "style of the music itself."[260] Murcia confirms his intuition in declaring that its execution is always "on the fret where the finger is lifted,"[261] implying that the trill must be executed on the upper auxiliary note both in Spanish and French pieces. Nonetheless, perhaps the fact that he feels compelled to specify this supposes the existence of alternatives around him, so that this feature might reflect, as Strizich had suggested, his close contact with French music instead of a common practice among Spanish guitarists of his time.

On the other hand, in addition to his recommendation of strumming delicately, Murcia is very clear in characterizing his music as a professional and refined practice:

> This explanation may give some knowledge as to executing the graces and ornaments of this instrument (as unique), which constitute the soul of the performance; but, notwithstanding, it would be impossible for the amateur with good taste, and who is not lazy, to take as much advantage from it as from listening to an expert performing them, who can verbally instruct him in the fundamental principles; unlike those congregated among the number of punchers or acorn pickers who try to stimulate the sense of hearing by hitting the guitar. God save us from this summer hail.[262]

In this manner, he distances himself from the popular use of the guitar, perhaps motivated by the usual disdain that some people expressed about it from around 1600 onward (which led to the well-known defense of the instrument by several guitarists during the seventeenth century, such as Amat and Doici).[263] But this attitude may also reflect his contact with elite groups, both in serving as guitar teacher to the queen and, hypothetically, to aristocratic members of Madrid society (Andriani, Pedro and Íñigo de Garaicoechea, etc.) throughout his life. This supports the hypothesis that even though his pieces incorporate features (genres, styles) of popular music, they are related more closely to high culture. Therefore, the practice by some contemporary performers of filling these pieces with percussion instruments and other effects emphasizing their popular traits should be the object of further reflections, at least from a historical point of view.[264] On the contrary, given that Murcia's *diferencias* can be interpreted as a form of written improvisations, as commented above, the current practice of performing them in a relatively free way, adding variations or improvising on Murcia's text, appears to be historically grounded. Furthermore, "Cifras selectas de guitarra" provides the performer with alternative settings of some *diferencias* already known through "Códice Saldívar" and "Passacalles y obras," which constitutes an invaluable opportunity to combine them in a creative way.

Finally, the distinction previously made between dances in a strict sense and instrumental pieces inspired by dance types, as most of Murcia's "dances" indeed are, also has an important implication for the performer: if a piece is neither linked to choreography nor any performance outside itself, the flexibility in the field of velocity and rhythm increases. Obviously, the extent to which such liberty—and others commented on above—might distance a performance from Murcia's style is also part of the problem.

Appendix

The following abbreviations are used in table 2:

ASC	Antonio de Santa Cruz, "Livro donde se verán pazacalles de los ocho tonos," M. 2209, Biblioteca Nacional de Madrid.
CAMP	François Campion, *Nouvelles découvertes sur la guitarre* (1705; facsimile edition, with an introduction by François Lesure, Geneva: Minkoff Reprint, 1977).
CORB	Francesco Corbetta, *La guitarre royale* (1670; facsimile edition, Geneva: Minkoff Reprint, 1975).
CSA	[Santiago de Murcia], *Saldívar Codex No. 4* (facsimile edition, with an introduction by Michael Lorimer, Santa Barbara: n.p., 1987).
CSG	Santiago de Murcia, "Cifras selectas de guitarra," Pontificia Universidad Católica de Chile, Biblioteca Campus Oriente.
FM	Antonio Martín y Coll, "Flores de música, obras y versos de varios organistas," M. 1357, Biblioteca Nacional de Madrid. I have not checked this source yet. The concordances come from Craig H. Russell, "Santiago de Murcia: Spanish Theorist and

	Guitarist of the Early Eighteenth Century" (Ph.D. diss., University of North Carolina at Chapel Hill, 1981).
GS	Gaspar Sanz, *Instrucción de música sobre la guitarra española* (1674, 1697; facsimile edition, with an introduction by Luis García-Abrines, Zaragoza: Institución Fernando el Católico, 1966).
LC	"Recueil des pièces de guitarre composées para Mr. François Le Cocq" (1730; facsimile edition in vol. 1 of *Thesaurus musicus, nova series*, series A, Brussels: Alamire, 1979).
LDC	"Libro de diferentes cifras de guitara" (1705), M. 811, Biblioteca Nacional de Madrid.
LRR	Lucas Ruiz de Ribayaz, *Luz y norte musical para caminar por las cifras de la guitarra española* (Madrid: Melchor Álvarez, 1677).
LTCA	"Libro de tonos puestos en cifra de arpa," M. 2478, Biblioteca Nacional de Madrid.
M. M. 97	M. M. 97, Biblioteca Geral da Universidade de Coimbra. I have not consulted this source yet; the concordance has been identified from the transcription of Rogério Budasz, "The Five-course Guitar (Viola) in Portugal and Brazil in the Late Seventeenth and Early Eighteenth Centuries" (Ph.D. diss., University of Southern California, 2001), 338.
Ms. 1560	Ms. 1560, Biblioteca Nacional de México.
PO	Santiago de Murcia, *Passacalles y obras de guitarra por todos los tonos naturales y accidentales* (1732; facsimile edition, with an introduction by Michael Macmeeken, Monaco: Éditions Chanterelle, 1979).
RA	Santiago de Murcia, *Resumen de acompañar la parte con la guitarra* (1714; facsimile edition, with an introduction by Monica Hall, Monaco: Éditions Chanterelle, 1980).
SMF	Music of Juan Francisco Tejera's *Sarao de la minué francés*, as edited in Carmelo Caballero, *"Arded, corazón, arded": Tonos humanos del Barroco en la Península Ibérica* (Valladolid: Las Edades del Hombre, 1997), 153–55.
VIS	Robert de Visée, *Les deux livres de guitarre: Paris 1682 et 1686*, ed. Hélène Charnassé, Rafael Andia, and Gérard Rebours (Paris: Éditions Transatlantiques, 1999).

TABLE 2
Contents and Concordances of "Cifras selectas de guitarra"

No.	Folio	Title of the Piece	Concordant Sources	Observations
1	1r	Jácaras por la E	CSA, 1r.	
2	2r	Marionas por la B	CSA, 3r.	The version in CSA shares two variations with a chaconne attributed to Corbetta in LC, 106–7.
3	3v	Difrencias de gallardas por la E	CSA, 4v.	
4	4v	Pavanas por la E		
5	6r	Españoletas por la E	CSA, 6r.	Some similarities with LDC, 104.
6	7v	Folías españolas por la E	CSA, 20v.	Some initial similarity with the *folías* of LDC, 105.
7	8v	Jácaras francesas por la D	CSA, 29r.	The beginning is similar to *jácaras francesas* of LDC, 127, and *Air* of CAMP, 81.
8	9v	El Amor por la E	CSA, 27v.	Similar to LDC, 113, which does not include variations.
9	10r	Tarantelas por la E	CSA, 18v.	
10	11r	Las vacas por la E	CSA, 23v.	
11	13v	Folías despacio al estilo de Italia	CSA, 60v.	The beginning is very similar to *folías italianas* of LDC, 136.
12	18v	Pasacalles de compasillo por la E	PO, 23v.	
13	19v	A proporción por este tono	PO, 25v.	
14	20v	Villanos por la C	CSA, 7r.	
15	21r	Caballero por la C	CSA, 8r.	LDC, 105, has a *villano caballero*, also preceded by a *villano*.
16	22r	Paradetas por la C		The second variation in CSG is similar to that at the beginning of LDC, 109.

TABLE 2 continued

No.	Folio	Title of the Piece	Concordant Sources	Observations
17	23v	Canarios por la C	CSA, 9r.	The beginning is very similar to the *canarios* of LDC, 108.
18	24v	Menuet fácil	RA, 90; LDC, 116.	Same piece with some variants.
19	25r	Menuet		
20	25r	Otro [Menuet]	LDC, 134.	Same piece with some variants and a fourth lower.
21	25r	Otro [Menuet]		
22	25v	Otro [Menuet]	Ms. 1560, 23.	Same piece with some variants.
23	25v	Otro [Menuet]		
24	26r	Otro [Menuet]		
25	26r	Otro [Menuet]		
26	26v	El menuet inglés		
27	27r	Menuet		
28	27r	Otro [Menuet]		
29	27v	Otro [Menuet]		
30	27v	Otro [Menuet]		
31	28r	Otro [Menuet] difícil		
32	28r	Otro [Menuet]		
33	28v	Otro [Menuet]		
34	28v	Otro [Menuet]		
35	29r	Jácaras de la costa	CSA, 39r.	
36	29v	El torneo por la C		Apart from the first section, it includes the following subsections: "Batallas," "Reverencias," and "Últimas reverencias." The last two are a reprise of the ending of the first section. The same *batalla* with some variants appears in LDC, 80; GS, lxxxiii; and LRR, 90 (copy of GS). The "Reverencias" are equivalent to "Retiradas" in the *torneo* of LDC, 80. See also GS, lxxxiii, and LRR, 89. The version of LDC is the most similar to that of CSG.
36	30v	———: Jácaras del torneo		Melodic coincidences with "Jácaras sobre la C" of ASC, 3r. Murcia appends this dance and the following to the standardized structure of the *torneo*.
36	31r	———: Gallardas del torneo	LDC, 83.	The last variation in LDC is virtually identical to the penultimate variation in CSG. Cf. a transcription of the former in Maurice Esses, *Dance and Instrumental* Diferencias *in Spain During the 17th and Early 18th Centuries* (Stuyvesant, N.Y.: Pendragon Press, 1992), 2:281. Two measures in the second variation of "Gallardas por la C" of ASC, 9r, are concordant with the fourth of CSG.
37	31v	La Azucena por la E	SMF; LTCA, 11r.	The version in LTCA is more similar to that of SMF than CSG. There is also a piece entitled "La Azucena, o minuet" in Sebastián de Aguirre's "Método de cítara" (= "Códice Saldívar no. 2"), according to Antonio Corona's inventory. I have not been able to consult it.
38	32r	Los imposibles por la D	CSA, 12v.	Only brief fragments of both versions coincide. The one in CSG lacks the last part as folio 33 is missing. I have completed it on the basis of CSA.
	[33r]	[Canarios por la A]	CSA, 10r?	Piece lost as folio 33 is missing.
39	[33v]	Cumbé por la A	CSA, 43r; LDC, 46.	The beginning of this piece is missing as folio 33 was torn out. I have completed it on the basis of CSA, excluding its strummed introduction, which is almost identical to that of the *paracumbé* of LDC. The latter also has a passage in common with CSG. The concordance is highly significant.
40	35r	Zarambeques por la C	CSA, 45r.	
41	35v	Obra por la C: Alemanda		

TABLE 2 continued

No.	Folio	Title of the Piece	Concordant Sources	Observations
41	36r	———: Correnta		
41	36v	———: Zarabanda	LDC, 35.	Same piece with some variants. The title of "Zarabanda francesa por la C" in LDC may refer to its style or indicate its origin from a French source. Shares the initial motif with VIS, 115, and CORB, 40.
41	37r	———: Giga	M. M. 97, 91r.	Transcribed in Budasz, "The Five-course Guitar," 338.
42	37v	Bailad caracoles por la C	CSA, 11v.	
43	38r	Marsellas por la B	CSA, 56v; RA, 107.	
44	39v	Canción		
45	40r	Marcha de los oboes	LDC, 120–21.	The piece in LDC is entitled "Aboe."
46	40r	Marcha valona		
47	40v	Marcha de los carabineros		Similar to "Marcha de carabineros" of LDC, 130.
48	41v	Marcha de las guardias de la Reina Ana		
	[42r]	[Paspied viejo]	CSA, 79r; RA, 57?	Piece lost as folio 42 is missing.
49	[42v]	Paspied nuevo	CSA, 79v; RA, 57?	The beginning of the piece is lost as folio 42 is missing. I have completed it on the basis of CSA and RA.
50	43r	Burée por la D		
51	43v	Gavota		
52	43v	Gavota	PO, 109r; LC, 10.	The ending of this piece is lost as folio 44 is missing. I have completed it on the basis of PO.
53	45r	Idea nueva, y obra especial de clarines: Idea nueva de clarines primorosos por la C	PO, 58r.	The title "Idea nueva, y obra especial de clarines" appears in the list of contents. This piece, as well as "Idea de dos clarines" that appears later (fol. 48v), has variations in common with that of PO. It shares some passages with FM, 76, according to Russell, "Santiago de Murcia: Spanish Theorist."
53	46r	———: Canción airosa	PO, 63r.	
53	46r	———: Llamadas	PO, 63v.	
53	47r	———: Marcha	PO, 65r; FM, 85.	
53	48r	———: Canción de ecos	PO, 64v–65r; FM, 50, 96, 173, 270.	
53	48r	———: Fajina	PO, 66v; FM, 84.	
53	48v	———: Idea de dos clarines	PO, 58r.	Fragments of this piece and that of folio 45r are found in PO.
54	50v	Obra por la K3: Preludio por la K3 que es lo mismo que la L	PO, 124v; CAMP, 50.	The title "Obra por la K3" figures in the list of contents. In PO the prelude is a half-step lower, and in CAMP a step higher.
54	51r	———: Alemanda	CAMP, 50.	Same piece, a step higher.
54	51v	———: Correnta	CAMP, 56	
54	52r	———: [Zarabanda]	CAMP, 57.	
54	52r	———: Giga	CAMP, 51	Same piece, a step higher.
55	52v	Burée	PO, 108v; LC, 53.	The piece in PO is the same. On the contrary, only some passages concord with LC.
56	53r	Pasacalles de compasillo por la O	PO, 43v.	
57	54r	A proporción	PO, 45v; LDC, 48–49.	In LDC the first variations coincide, but in a different order.
58	55r	Pasacalles de compasillo por el +	PO, 4r.	
59	56v	A proporción	GS, cvi.	Though these are different pieces, variation 7 of CSG is a quotation of variation 5 of a *pasacalle* by Sanz. Variation 3 of both pieces is also very similar.
60	57v	Pasacalles de compasillo por la B		
61	58r	A proporción	PO, 12r.	
62	59r	Pasacalles de compasillo por la G	PO, 30r.	

TABLE 2 continued

No.	Folio	Title of the Piece	Concordant Sources	Observations
63	61r	A proporción	PO, 32r.	
64	62r	Pasacalles de compasillo por la D	PO, 20r.	
65	63v	A proporción	PO, 22r.	
66	64v	Pasacalles aclarinados por la C a compasillo	PO, 13v.	
67	66r	Pasacalles a compasillo por la H	PO, 33r.	
68	67v	A proporción	PO, 35r.	
69	68v	Pasacalles de compasillo por la A	PO, 7v.	
70	69v	A proporción	PO, 9r.	
	[73]	[Obra de alemanda, correnta, y giga por la E]		Pieces lost as final folios are missing.
	[74]	[Obra de Coreli, de alemanda, correnta, zarabanda, y giga por la E]		Pieces lost.
	[77]	[Otra obra de Coreli, de grave, o preludio, alemanda y dos gigas por el +]		Pieces lost.
	[81]	[Difrentes piezas por la B]		Pieces lost.

Note. The spelling of the titles has been modernized where the original has no phonetic value, and the abbreviations have been expanded.

Notes

The following abbreviations and sigla are used in the notes:

ACS	Santiago, Chile, Archivo Catedralicio
AFS	Santiago, Chile, Archivo Franciscano
AHA	Santiago, Chile, Archivo Histórico del Arzobispado
AMS	Santiago, Chile, Archivo Mercedario
ANH	Santiago, Chile, Archivo Nacional Histórico
DMEH	*Diccionario de la música española e hispanoamericana*, ed. Emilio Casares (Madrid: SGAE, 1999–2002)
DRAE	*Diccionario de la lengua castellana . . . . Compuesto por la Real Academia Española*
E-Mah	Madrid, Archivo Histórico Nacional
E-Mahd	Madrid, Archivo Histórico Diocesano
E-Mahp	Madrid, Archivo Histórico de Protocolos
E-Mapsg	Madrid, Archivo Parroquial de San Ginés
E-Mapss	Madrid, Archivo Parroquial de San Sebastián
E-Mav	Madrid, Archivo de Villa
E-Mn	Madrid, Biblioteca Nacional
E-Mp	Madrid, Archivo General del Palacio Real
E-Sagi	Seville, Archivo General de Indias
NG2	*The New Grove Dictionary of Music and Musicians*, 2nd edition
NTLLE	Nuevo tesoro lexicográfico de la lengua castellana, available at http://buscon.rae.es/ntlle/SrvltGUILoginNtlle (it includes digital copies of the dictionaries published by the Real Academia Española from 1726 onwards)
PARES	Portal de Archivos Españoles, available at http://pares.mcu.es (including digital copies of documents from Spanish archives)

1. I published an initial and brief account of this source in Alejandro Vera, "Una nueva fuente para la música del siglo XVIII: El manuscrito Cifras Selectas de Guitarra de Santiago de Murcia (1722)," *Resonancias* 18 (2006): 35–49. A deeper study was published later in Alejandro Vera, "Santiago de Murcia's *Cifras Selectas de Guitarra* (1722): A New Source for the Baroque Guitar," *Early Music* 35 (2007): 251–69. This introduction considerably expands the information presented there based on new documentary evidence and other data. An independent recording with pieces of this manuscript was carried out in 2007 by two of my colleagues; see Oscar Ohlsen and Eduardo Figueroa, *Cifras Selectas de Guitarra* (Santiago de Chile, 2007).

2. With respect to the recordings, see, among others, Rolf Lislevand (dir.), *Santiago de Murcia Codex* (Paris: Astrée, 2000); William Waters, *Santiago de Murcia: Passacalles y obras de guitarra* (Barcelona: La Mà de Guido, 1996); and Cristina Azuma, *Santiago de Murcia. A Portrait* (Florence: Frame, 2007). The main studies will be quoted below.

3. For a description of the instrument, see the editorial policies.

4. Santiago de Murcia, *Resumen de acompañar la parte con la guitarra* (1714; facsimile edition, with an introduction by Monica Hall, Monaco: Éditions Chanterelle, 1980). Unless otherwise indicated, all the references to that book are based on this edition. There is also a facsimile edition with an introduction by

Gerardo Arriaga (Madrid: Arte Tripharia, 1984). In the present work I keep the spelling of the titles of manuscript and edited sources, but, in the titles of the pieces, the spelling has been modernized when the original has no phonetic value, and the abbreviations have been expanded.

5. Nicolas Morales, *L'Artiste de cour dans l'Espagne du XVIIIe siècle: Étude de la communauté des musiciens au service de Philippe V (1700–1746)* (Madrid: Casa de Velázquez, 2007), 162, 199. These documents confirm that Murcia was the guitar teacher referred to by the duke of Gramont and the queen in two letters written in 1704 and 1705; see, respectively, Maurice Esses, *Dance and Instrumental Diferencias in Spain During the 17th and Early 18th Centuries* (Stuyvesant, N.Y.: Pendragon Press, 1992), 1:132; and Elena Machado Lowenfeld, "Santiago de Murcia's Thorough-bass Treatise for the Baroque Guitar (1714): Introduction, Translation, and Transcription" (master's thesis, City University of New York, 1975), 4.

6. I have published an initial study on these aspects in "Santiago de Murcia (1673–1739): New Contributions on His Life and Work," *Early Music* 36 (2008): 597–608. For more extended references and transcriptions of some relevant documents, I encourage the reader to consult this article.

7. The term *violero* made reference to an instrument maker in a general sense, while *guitarrero* referred specifically to a guitar maker.

8. This hypothesis was originally raised by Lowenfeld, "Santiago de Murcia's Thorough-bass Treatise," 5, and subsequently developed by Craig H. Russell, "Santiago de Murcia: Spanish Theorist and Guitarist of the Early Eighteenth Century" (Ph.D. diss., University of North Carolina at Chapel Hill, 1981), 1:60–64. See also *Santiago de Murcia's "Códice Saldívar No. 4": A Treasury of Secular Guitar Music from Baroque Mexico*, ed. Craig H. Russell [with complete facsimile] (Urbana and Chicago: University of Illinois Press, 1995), 1:122–29.

9. Morales, *L'Artiste de cour*, 188.

10. "Libro de Bautismos de esta Parroquia de San Sebastián" (28 July 1673 to 29 September 1679), fol. 4v, E-Mapss. Besides, he was baptized on 9 August and his godfather was one Diego García.

11. Protocolo 15294, fols. 166r–166v, E-Mahp.

12. See "Matrícula parroquial de San Ginés" (1721) and "Libro 14 de Defunciones," fols. 380r, 381r, 415r, both in E-Mapsg. Matías de Murcia's declaration of poverty is preserved in Protocolo 14817, fols. 404r–404v, E-Mahp, but it does not offer any information about the guitarist. The death certificate of Magdalena Hernández informs us that she made her declaration of poverty in the presence of Hipólito Suazo y Urbina on 16 May 1721. Unfortunately, the deeds of this scribe for that year are lost in E-Mahp.

13. Expedientes matrimoniales, notario Manuel de San Martín (1695), E-Mahd.

14. Expedientes matrimoniales, notario Manuel de San Martín (1705), E-Mahd.

15. Parroquia de San Martín, "Índice de bautizados desde 1545 hasta 1682," E-Mahd.

16. See Morales, *L'Artiste de cour*, 29, and Begoña Lolo, *La música en la Real Capilla de Madrid: José de Torres y Martínez Bravo (h. 1670–1738)* (Madrid: Universidad Autónoma de Madrid, 1988), 70–72.

17. That was the case, for example, of the Carmelite convent (Carmen Calzado), at least since the beginning of the seventeenth century; see my book *Música vocal profana en el Madrid de Felipe IV: El "Libro de Tonos Humanos" (1656)* (Lleida: Institut d' Estudis Ilerdencs, 2002), 49–64. For a later epoch, the *villancicos* texts printed during the eighteenth century prove the existence in Madrid of musical chapels in La Merced, San Cayetano, San Felipe, and the Jesuit College (Colegio Imperial). See Álvaro Torrente, "Cuestiones en torno a la circulación de los músicos catedralicios en la España moderna," *Artigrama* 12 (1996–97): 219.

18. *Santiago de Murcia's "Códice Saldívar No. 4,"* 1:120–22.

19. Francisco Guerau, *Poema harmonico compuesto de varias cifras* (Madrid: Imprenta de Manuel Ruiz de Murga, 1694).

20. It must be pointed out that this appointment is not mentioned in Antoni Pizá, *Frances Guerau I el seu temps* (Palma: Govern de les Illes Balears, 2000), 24–25. The author only states that Guerau was appointed as master of the choirboys of the Royal College in June 1694, a reference also quoted by Russell.

21. This subject remains to a great extent unexplored. Notwithstanding, Gaspar Sanz published a eulogy in praise of Pope Innocent XI (*Ecos Sagrados*) in 1681 in Madrid, and he possibly died there at the beginning of the eighteenth century; see Gaspar Sanz, *Instrucción de música sobre la guitarra española* (1674, 1697; facsimile edition, with an introduction by Luis García-Abrines, Zaragoza: Institución Fernando el Católico, 1966), xvii. Additionally, Jean Baptiste de Castillion affirms in his preface to the "Recueil des pièces de guitarre" that his father had studied in Madrid with the Spanish guitarist Miguel Pérez de Zavala in about 1690. Nothing else is known about him; see "Recueil des pièces de guitarre" (1730; facsimile edition in vol. 1 of *Thesaurus musicus, nova series*, series A, Brussels: Alamire, 1979).

22. About Antonio de Murcia, see Expedientes matrimoniales, notario Manuel de San Martín (1702), E-Mahd; José L. Romanillos and Marian Harris Winspear, *The Vihuela de mano and the Spanish Guitar: A Dictionary of the Makers of Plucked and Bowed Musical Instruments of Spain (1200–2002)* (Guijosa: The Sanguino Press, 2002), 264; and Morales, *L'Artiste de cour*, 189.

23. See Vera, "Santiago de Murcia (1673–1739)," 600.

24. Morales, *L'Artiste de cour*, 3–8.

25. Ibid., 188. In the transcription of historical documents I modernize the spelling when it has no phonetic value, as well as the accents and punctuation.

26. Reinados, Felipe V, Legajo 220, E-Mp.

27. Morales, *L'Artiste de cour*, 72. A synthesis of the political conflicts of that time and some of their implications for music can be found in Álvaro Torrente, "The Sacred Villancico in Early Eighteenth-century Spain: The Repertory of Salamanca Cathedral" (Ph.D. diss., University of Cambridge, 1997), 1:1–19.

28. Morales, *L'Artiste de cour*, 79.

29. Monica Hall, "The Guitar Anthologies of Santiago de Murcia" (Ph.D. diss., The Open University, 1983), 1:63.

30. Russell, "Santiago de Murcia: Spanish Theorist," 1:40–46.

31. Ibid., 41; and *Santiago de Murcia's "Códice Saldívar No. 4,"* 1:116–17.

32. *Libro primero de los asientos de las casas de Madrid que comprehende cien manzanas desde el número primero hasta el ciento inclusive*, vol. 1 of *Planimetría general de Madrid* (ca. 1750; reprint, Madrid: Tabapress, 1988), 57, 59, 288. The last reference does not mention Andriani as such, but the position that he held: "Envoy from the Catholic Cantons" (Al Señor Embiado de los Cantones Catholicos).

33. Russell, "Santiago de Murcia: Spanish Theorist," 1:47.

34. James Tyler and Paul Sparks, *The Guitar and Its Music from the Renaissance to the Classical Era* (Oxford and New York: Oxford University Press, 2002), 159.

35. On the importance of Feuillet and this sort of repertory in Murcia's *Resumen de acompañar* and other sources, see Russell, "Santiago de Murcia: Spanish Theorist," 1:142–59.

36. Among the sources for other instruments, an important precedent is *Canciones francesas, de todos ayres, para todos los instrumentos*, printed in Madrid in 1701. See a description in Esses, *Dance and Instrumental Diferencias in Spain*, 1:334–35.

37. For instance, the recitative was already in fashion in Spanish court theater of the mid-seventeenth century; there was a progressive introduction in the court of musical groups linked to the trio sonata at least since ca. 1677; Marie Louise of Orleans, some time after her marriage to Charles II, brought an ensemble from Fontainebleau composed of several instrumentalists and singers; and Gaspar Sanz had already included some pieces in the French style. See Louise K. Stein, *Songs of Mortals, Dialogues of the Gods: Music and Theatre in Seventeenth Century Spain* (Oxford: Clarendon Press, 1993), 130ff.; Pablo Rodríguez,

"Música, poder y devoción: La capilla real de Carlos II (1665–1700)" (Ph.D. diss., University of Zaragoza, 2003), 4ff.; Morales, *L'Artiste de cour*, 154–55; and Sanz, *Instrucción de música*, lxxxviii.

38. See a complete account in Morales, *L'Artiste de cour*, 129–57.

39. For example, in November 1682 the duke of Veragua, in Seville, requested the music of Calderón's *Celos aún del aire matan* and *La estatua de Prometeo* from his cousin, the duke of Pastrana, in Madrid. See Louise K. Stein, "De la contera del mundo: las navegaciones de la ópera entre dos mundos y varias culturas," in *La ópera en España e Hispanoamérica*, ed. Emilio Casares and Álvaro Torrente (Madrid: ICCMU, 2001), 1:89.

40. Registros, Libro 185, fols. 198r, 214v, 236r, 285r, E-Mp. There is more information about Fonton in Morales, *L'Artiste de cour*, 162, 199.

41. Morales, *L'Artiste de cour*, 186–90.

42. Secretaría, Sección 1, legajo 386, n°1 (no foliation), E-Mav. For El Príncipe, see, among others, Secretaría, Sección 1, legajo 402, n°1 (1 July 1713). On the *contredanse* and its important cultivation in Spain during the eighteenth century, see Esses, *Dance and Instrumental Diferencias in Spain*, 1:454–60.

43. See Murcia, *Resumen de acompañar*. On these dances see *Santiago de Murcia's "Códice Saldívar No. 4,"* 1:52–55, 60–64, and 92–93.

44. Aside from the cited dissertations by Hall and Russell, see Santiago de Murcia, *Passacalles y obras de guitarra por todos los tonos naturales y accidentales* (1732; facsimile edition, with an introduction by Michael Macmeeken, Monaco: Éditions Chanterelle, 1979); and Neil D. Pennington, "The Development of Baroque Guitar Music in Spain, Including a Commentary on and a Transcription of Santiago de Murcia's 'Passacalles y obras' (1732)" (Ph.D. diss., University of Maryland, 1979), 1:272–336. There is also a partial transcription to modern notation in Santiago de Murcia, *Suites del libro "Passacalles y obras por todos los tonos naturales y accidentales" 1732*, vol. 4 of Santiago de Murcia, *Obras completas para guitarra*, ed. Antonio Company (Madrid: Soneto, 1995).

45. Monica Hall suggests a possible connection between the presence of pieces by Le Cocq and Murcia's trip to the Low Countries in 1714, for printing his *Resumen de acompañar*; see Hall, "The Guitar Anthologies," 1:63.

46. See Hall, "The Guitar Anthologies," 1:489–507, and Craig H. Russell and Astrid K. Topp Russell, "El arte de recomposición en la música española para guitarra barroca," *Revista de musicología* 5 (1982): 15–18.

47. The manuscript is presently owned by Saldívar's heirs. Apart from the quoted edition by Russell, see *Saldívar Codex No. 4* (facsimile edition, with an introduction by Michael Lorimer, Santa Barbara: n.p., 1987).

48. *Saldívar Codex No. 4*, v.

49. "Será al mostraros la ciencia / mi pauta la claridad . . ." See a reproduction in *Santiago de Murcia's "Códice Saldívar No. 4,"* 2:3, and *Saldívar Codex No. 4*. I have not been able to decode the entire riddle.

50. On the differentiation between these terms, see, among others, *Santiago de Murcia's "Códice Saldívar No. 4,"* 1:12–16. We shall return to this point later.

51. It does not include *pasacalles*, but only a table at the beginning with their strummed harmonic progression in each mode, both in duple and triple meter.

52. Hall, "The Guitar Anthologies," 1:65. This hypothesis is also discussed by Russell in *Santiago de Murcia's "Códice Saldívar No. 4,"* 1:133–35.

53. Robert Stevenson, "Santiago de Murcia: A Review Article," *Inter-American Music Review* 3, no. 1 (1980): 92–93.

54. Gerardo Arriaga, "Un manuscrito mexicano de música barroca," *Revista de musicología* 5 (1982): 115–21.

55. Hall, "The Guitar Anthologies," 1:93. The extant copies of this source are described in Juan Antonio de Vargas y Guzmán, *Explicación de la guitarra*, ed. A. Medina Álvarez (1773; Granada: Centro de Documentación Musical de Andalucía, 1994), xiii–xiv.

56. See Protocolo 15582, fols. 35r–35v (declaration of poverty of Josefa García) and fols. 58r–58v (declaration of poverty of Santiago de Murcia), E-Mahp.

57. Reinados, Felipe V, Legajo 220, E-Mp.

58. It was not the only occasion when Murcia complained about his fate. In the abovementioned *décima* in "Códice Saldívar" he stated: ". . . and I hope, my Lord, you put / the clef in your favor / the change in my fortune" (y espero pongáis señor / la clave en vuestro favor / la mutanza en mi fortuna).

59. As proven by the death certificate of his wife, preserved in Libro 15 de difuntos de la parroquia de San Martín (1725–1731), fol. 221r, E-Mahd.

60. Libro 17 de difuntos de la parroquia de San Martín (1738–1743), fol. 100v, E-Mahd.

61. ". . . y así mismo lo suplica a los señores Pedro Juan y don Íñigo de Garay y Cochea, don Joseph de Quesada y don Manuel de Pereda, a quienes pide que por amor de Dios hagan por su alma el bien que pudieren, y se le entreguen a los susodichos los papeles de música que el otorgante tiene, en comemoración [sic] del mucho amor que a los susodichos ha tenido." Murcia's declaration of poverty is cited in note 56 above.

62. Registros, libro 144, fol. 171v, E-Mp. His surname appears both as Perea and Pereda. The document does not indicate the year, but it seems obvious that it hints at the abovementioned journey of 1706.

63. There are two records about the entrance of Manuel Francisco de Pereda e Izquierdo into the Order of Santiago in OM-Caballeros_Santiago, Exp. 6341, and OM-Expedientillos, N. 5802, both in E-Mah. Since, according to the first record, Pereda e Izquierdo was born in 1657 (fol. 15r), it is also possible that the man mentioned in Murcia's declaration of poverty (1729) was his son, Manuel Antonio de Pereda, who signs a brief document in OM-Expedientillos, N. 5802 (no foliation). According to it, he lived in the port of Cadiz about 1747, which represents another possible link between our composer and Latin America.

64. Filipinas 58, N. 1, E-Sagi, available at PARES (accessed 11 June 2008).

65. Órdenes Militares, Caballeros de Santiago, expediente 3260, E-Mah, available at PARES (accessed 11 June 2008).

66. Contratación 5468, N.1, R.1, E-Sagi, available at PARES (accessed 11 June 2008).

67. Protocolo 15102, E-Mahp.

68. Ibid., fols. 207r–212r.

69. Specifically on the island of Bohol, which he inherited from his maternal grandfather, Sebastián de Villarreal. See Filipinas 58, N. 1, cited in note 64 above.

70. M. 811, "Libro de diferentes cifras de guitara" (1705), E-Mn. I was able to consult the edition by Francisco Alfonso Valdivia only as the present book was going to press. See *Libro de diferentes cifras M/811 (1705)*, ed. Francisco Alfonso Valdivia (Madrid: Sociedad de la Vihuela, 2008).

71. For the editorial policies explaining some particularities of my transcriptions (such as the cue notes), see the critical report.

72. This correspondence was also noticed by Rogério Budasz, "Black Guitar-players and Early African-Iberian Music in Portugal and Brazil," *Early Music* 35 (2007): 15. See also his dissertation, "The Five-course Guitar (Viola) in Portugal and Brazil in the Late Seventeenth and Early Eighteenth Centuries" (Ph.D. diss., University of Southern California, 2001), 159.

73. Despite the interesting evidence provided by Russell about their cultivation in Mexico; see *Santiago de Murcia's "Códice Saldívar No. 4,"* 1:69–79.

74. Budasz, "Black Guitar-players," 5.

75. On the *cumbé* see Morales, *L'Artiste de cour*, 91 (the document of Pedro París y Royo), and *Santiago de Murcia's "Códice Saldívar No. 4,"* 1:72. Additionally, a "danza de negros" was performed in 1669, during the festivities for the canonization of Saint Maria Magdalena de Pazzi in Madrid; see Vera, *Música vocal profana*, 59.

76. See Lolo, *La música en la Real Capilla de Madrid*, 56.

77. This was not new at that time. After the death of the Carmelite composer Fr. Manuel Correa, in 1653, the Zaragoza cathedral demanded ownership of his music papers because he was considered the best composer of *villancicos* in Spain ("el primero en gracia para los villancicos"). The Carmelite convent of that city also claimed to have the right to his scores. See Pedro Calahorra Martínez, *La Música en Zaragoza* (Zaragoza: Institución Fernando el Católico, 1978), 2:101.

78. As explained in Morales, *L'Artiste de cour*, 5.

79. The only publication I have found on García Burr and his collection is a magazine article by María Paz Larraín, "El grupo de Los Diez," *Revista ED* 52 (2000): 90–97.

80. The inventory was kindly sent to me by Carlos Salinas, an employee of the auction house. It includes a book entitled *La guitarra* by Segundo N. Contreras (Buenos Aires, 1927), among other titles related to music.

81. See, for example, the word "Alemanda" in the last column of the table of contents and the title on fol. 51r.

82. The expression "por la E" and others like it refer to the *alfabeto* system for the guitar, described below in "The Music: Notation and Theory."

83. See Hall, "The Guitar Anthologies," 1:67, and Stevenson, "Santiago de Murcia," 92.

84. See her introduction to Murcia, *Resumen de acompañar*, iii.

85. *Santiago de Murcia's "Códice Saldívar No. 4,"* 1:193.

86. Hall describes an S linked with a P at the bottom; see Hall, "The Guitar Anthologies," 1:77. I have been able to examine a digital image of the watermark in "Códice Saldívar" which was kindly sent to me by the musicologist Antonio Corona (email of 20 February 2007).

87. It could also be due to the use of at least two molds to produce the paper, giving rise to a pair of very similar but not identical watermarks. But, in this case, the difference between them would probably be less important. There is a detailed study on these aspects and their application to Spanish music from the end of the eighteenth century in Germán Labrador, "El papel R. Romaní y la datación de la música española de finales del s. XVIII (1775–1800): Una nueva vía de investigación en la obra de L. Boccherini," *Revista de musicología* 27 (2004): 699–741.

88. Jan LaRue, "Watermarks and Musicology," *Acta musicologica* 33 (1961): 138–41. Also, Carmela Bongiovanni confirms having found this watermark in archival documents from Genoa, as well as several manuscript scores by Luigi Boccherini; see Carmela Bongiovanni, "Luigi Boccherini y Génova: Por una revisión de las fuentes musicales y documentales," in *Luigi Boccherini: Estudio sobre fuentes, recepción e historiografía*, ed. Marco Mangani, Elisabeth Le Guin, and Jaime Tortella (Madrid: Comunidad de Madrid, Dirección General de Archivos, Museos y Bibliotecas, 2006), 197. I am grateful to the author for drawing my attention to her article.

89. For example, "two reams of paper from Genoa" (dos resmas de papel de Génova) are mentioned in the Mercedarian convent of Santiago de Chile in 1710; see "Censos (1707–1749)," fol. 29r, AMS.

90. Legajo 1482 ("Felices mortales," 1743) and legajo 1484 ("Al que de pastorcito," 1748), E-Mn. See also Álvaro Torrente, *Fiesta de Navidad en la Capilla Real de Felipe V: Villancicos de Francisco Corselli, 1743* (Madrid: Fundación Caja Madrid, Alpuerto S.A., 2002), 43–48.

91. As I suggested in my article "Santiago de Murcia's *Cifras Selectas de Guitarra*," 254.

92. This list combines data from Morales, *L'Artiste de cour*, 37–38, and Torrente, *Fiesta de Navidad*, 49–51. The dates are approximate in most cases. Montalvo was the brother-in-law of the composer Antonio de Literes, who, as we have seen, wrote the approbation of *Resumen de acompañar* in 1717.

93. His signature is reproduced in Vera, "Santiago de Murcia (1673–1739)," 602. Compare it, for example, with fol. 34r of "Códice Saldívar."

94. Pablo Minguet e Yrol, *Reglas y advertencias generales que enseñan el modo de tañer todos los instrumentos mejores y más usuales como son la guitarra, tiple, vandola, cythara, clavicordio, organo, harpa, psalterio, bandurria, violín, flauta travesera, flauta dulce y la flautilla* (N.p.: n.p., n.d.). The place of publication is offered in the booklets comprising this treatise. The dates do not always coincide, but they range from 1752 to 1754. See also María Sanhuesa Fonseca, "Minguet e Yrol, Pablo," in *DMEH*, 7:588–92.

95. "In order to tune the guitar, bandurria, and violin, equalize the first string of the guitar with the first string of the violin and the second string of the bandurria; otherwise, it is better to match the third strings of the guitar stopped on the second fret with the second string of the violin; and the remaining guitar strings are tuned; and once it is well tuned, prepare the second major chord and play it a little, and if the three instruments do not sound as one voice, the violinist can adjust his second string and the bandurria player his first string, because their instruments are easier to tune." (Para poner acordes guitarra, bandurria y violín se igualan la prima de la guitarra con la prima del violín y con la segunda de la bandurria; o si no, mejor es igualar las terceras de la guitarra pisadas en 2 traste con la segunda del violín; y se templan las demás cuerdas de la guitarra; y después de bien templada, se hace el segundo punto natural y se tañe un poco, y si los 3 instrumentos no hacen una voz, el del violín puede ir igualando su segunda y el de la bandurria su prima, porque son más fáciles de templar.) Murcia, "Cifras selectas de guitarra," instructions for tuning the guitar. Compare with the translation of Minguet's eleventh rule by Christopher T. O'Dania, "The 'Academia Musical' of Pablo Minguet y Yrol: A Translation and Commentary (Spain)" (master's thesis, University of North Texas, 1984), 56.

96. "For tuning the guitar with the tiple, equalize the third strings of the tiple with the fourth strings of the guitar, so that they sound as a single voice, and the rest are tuned, no more and no less, as those of the guitar." (Para templar la guitarra con el tiple, se igualan las terceras del tiple con las cuartas de la guitarra, de suerte que hagan una misma voz, y las demás se templan, ni más ni menos, como las de la guitarra.) Murcia, "Cifras selectas de guitarra," instructions for tuning the guitar. Compare with O'Dania, "The 'Academia Musical' of Pablo Minguet y Yrol," 58.

97. According to Hall, "The Guitar Anthologies," 1:81.

98. According to Russell in *Santiago de Murcia's "Códice Saldívar No. 4,"* 1:4–5.

99. See Tyler and Sparks, *The Guitar and Its Music*, 64–66.

100. Murcia, *Passacalles y obras de guitarra*, front page. Russell identifies him hypothetically with Joseph Álvarez del Valle, a knight of the Order of Santiago who lived in Madrid in the first half of the eighteenth century; see *Santiago de Murcia's "Códice Saldívar No. 4,"* 1:117–19. The *décima* in "Códice Saldívar" could be dedicated to him if both manuscripts indeed correspond to a single anthology.

101. "In having made these pages open, it was my only desire to intensify the pleasure of guitar lovers, giving them, with novelty, the proper incentive to study. To them, particularly, this book is offered . . ." (En haber hecho abrir estas láminas, llevó por único fin mi deseo, el avivar el gusto de los aficionados a la guitarra, dándoles con la novedad el más propio incentivo de la aplicación. A éstos con singularidad se les ofrece el libro . . .) Murcia, *Resumen de acompañar*, prologue.

102. See Larraín, "El grupo de Los Diez," 96. This has been confirmed by his two children, Gabriela and Eduardo García Powditch, interviewed by telephone on 21 June and 31 October 2006.

103. "Tampoco me detengo en explicar las gracias que hay en ejecutar, las cuales son la sal de lo que se tañe (aunque van figuradas), persuadido a que no habrá aficionado que no haya visto el libro tan singular que dio a la estampa Don Francisco Garau (de tañidos de España, y pasacalles primorosos), en el cual pone al principio toda la explicación, con notable luz y

conocimiento, para el que quisiere manejar este instrumento; con todas las feligranas que pueden caber en la última destreza." See Murcia, *Resumen de acompañar,* prologue.

104. Lucas Ruiz de Ribayaz, *Luz y norte musical para caminar por las cifras de la guitarra española* (Madrid: Melchor Álvarez, 1677), prologue. I am citing the translation of Esses, *Dance and Instrumental Diferencias in Spain,* 1:3–4.

105. Contratación 674, fol. 185r, E-Sagi. This reference has been quoted by Jania Sarno, "El tráfico de instrumentos y libros musicales de España al Nuevo Mundo a través de los documentos del Archivo General de Indias de Sevilla: Notas para el comienzo de una investigación," in *Musiques et influences culturelles réciproques entre l'Europe et l'Amérique Latine du XVIème au XXème siècle,* ed. René de Maeyer (Brussels: The Brussels Museum of Musical Instruments, 1986), 99.

106. Contratación 674, fol. 493v, E-Sagi.

107. Ibid., fols. 68r, 84r, 155r, 182r, 333v, 728v (Torres), 929r, 930r (Ulloa), 930v (Torres), 931r (Nasarre). The folios without further indication include references to Lorente's book. The first of these was quoted by Sarno, "El tráfico de instrumentos y libros musicales de España al Nuevo Mundo," 99.

108. Contratación 674, fol. 227r, E-Sagi.

109. Diversos-Colecciones, 43, N. 44, fol. 1r, E-Mah, available at PARES (accessed 24 June 2008). About the identity of Murillo and the circumstances of his trip, see Actas del Definitorio, vol. 3, fols. 224r, 245v, AFS.

110. Diversos-Colecciones, 45, N. 48, fol. 2r, E-Mah, available at PARES (accessed 24 June 2008).

111. Juan Pablo Fernández-Cortés, *La música en las casas de Osuna y Benavente (1733–1882): Un estudio sobre el mecenazgo musical de la alta nobleza española* (Madrid: Sociedad Española de Musicología, 2007), 106–7.

112. Protocolo 14609, fol. 148r, E-Mahp. Andriani also held close contacts with Mexico. For additional references see my article "Santiago de Murcia's *Cifras Selectas de Guitarra,*" 252–53.

113. Contratación 1700 (no foliation), E-Sagi. These instruments apparently came from Genoa. It must be stated that the final inventory only mentions four organs.

114. See my article "¿Decadencia o progreso? La música del siglo XVIII y el nacionalismo decimonónico," *Latin American Music Review* 31 (2010): 1–39. In addition, the presence of *Lecciones de clave y principios de harmonia* by Benito Bails (Madrid, 1775) is mentioned by Eugenio Pereira Salas, *Los orígenes del arte musical en Chile* (Santiago: Imprenta Universitaria, 1941), 155.

115. See Alejandro Vera, "A propósito de la recepción de música y músicos extranjeros en el Chile colonial," *Cuadernos de Música Iberoamericana* 10 (2005): 29.

116. Escribanos de Santiago, vol. 387, fol. 402r; vol. 719, fol. 404r; vol. 820, fol. 335r; and vol. 522, fol. 237r, ANH.

117. See Julio Retamal Ávila, *Testamentos de "indios" en Chile colonial: 1564–1801* (Santiago: Universidad Andrés Bello, 2000), 219.

118. Alejandro Vera, "Music in the Monastery of La Merced, Santiago de Chile, in the Colonial Period," *Early Music* 32 (2004): 370, 375.

119. Jesuitas de Chile, vol. 24, fol. 304r, ANH.

120. Actas del Definitorio, vol. 1, fols. 53r, 82v, 113r, 142v, AFS.

121. Pereira Salas, *Los orígenes del arte musical en Chile,* 226.

122. In 1790 Miguel Galar embarked on the ship "El Diamante," bound for Iquique, Arica, and other northern ports, with "1000 handfuls of guitar strings" (1000 mazos de cuerdas de guitarra); Contaduría mayor, 1ª serie, vol. 1790, fol. 186r, ANH. Pereira Salas, *Los orígenes del arte musical en Chile,* 226, adds that in the store of Casimiro Pereyra in Córdova (Argentina) there were "six and a half grosses of guitar strings from Chile" (seis y media gruesas de cuerdas de Chile para guitarra).

123. Arribadas 439 A, Exp. 230, E-Sagi. Unfortunately, this record does not include an inventory of the objects he shipped.

124. Parroquia del Sagrario, Libro 6 de matrimonios, fol. 150r, AHA.

125. For example, in September 1838 he sold some fabrics to Santiago Cathedral; see Contaduría mayor, 1ª serie, vol. 1102, fol. 312r, ANH. His death certificate is preserved in "Libro 4 de defunciones de la Parroquia del Sagrario," fol. 32v, AHA.

126. *Melodías virreinales del siglo XVIII,* ed. Javier Echecopar (Lima: Carrillo-Echecopar, 1992), 7–8.

127. See Russell's transcription in *Santiago de Murcia's "Códice Saldívar No. 4,"* 2:271.

128. See, among others, *Saldívar Codex No. 4,* xvi–xix; *Santiago de Murcia's "Códice Saldívar No. 4,"* 2:xiii–xv; Russell, "Santiago de Murcia: Spanish Theorist," 1:128–41 and 2:v–x; Pennington, "The Development of Baroque Guitar Music in Spain," 1:88–101, 320, and 2:viii. There is also a useful synthesis of baroque guitar notation in Tyler and Sparks, *The Guitar and Its Music,* 165–83, and *The Baroque Guitar in Spain and the New World,* ed. Frank Koonce (Pacific, Mo.: Mel Bay Publications, 2006), 7–11.

129. Cf. *The Baroque Guitar in Spain,* 10.

130. Guerau, *Poema harmonico,* 4, calls it "temblor."

131. Cf. Pennington, "The Development of Baroque Guitar Music in Spain," 1:158–59.

132. Murcia, *Resumen de acompañar,* 42–44. Cf. Russell, "Santiago de Murcia: Spanish Theorist," 1:133–41, and Luis Gásser, "Murcia, Santiago de," in *DMEH,* 7:897–98.

133. See Vera, *Música vocal profana,* 145–46.

134. Murcia, *Resumen de acompañar,* 43. "En este tiempo hay variedad . . . . En el [estilo] de España cuando va despacio, en los semibreves, en las mínimas o semínimas (que valen lo mismo en dicho tiempo) se darán la primera, y la segunda llenas, y también en la última si pidiere postura."

135. Murcia, indeed, stated that the meter $\frac{3}{8}$ was used to indicate "arias muy promptas" (very fast arias); *Resumen de acompañar,* 44. In "Códice Saldívar" (fol. 45r) the "Zarambeques" are notated in $\frac{3}{4}$.

136. Vera, *Música vocal profana,* 144–45.

137. Murcia, *Resumen de acompañar,* 42.

138. Pablo Nasarre, *Fragmentos músicos* (1700; facsimile edition, Zaragoza: Institución Fernando el Católico, 1988), 270.

139. Castillion stated that such a symbol implied four quarter notes per measure but performed at double speed; see "Recueil des pièces de guitarre," 11. Valls also declared around 1741 that this sign was interpreted as a somewhat faster *compasillo* ("compasillo algo apresurado"); see Francisco Valls, "Mapa armónico práctico," Ms. 783, fol. 225r, Biblioteca de la Universidad de Barcelona (Spain).

140. Castillion, "Recueil des pièces de guitarre," 11.

141. See Valls, "Mapa armónico práctico," fols. 226r–227r.

142. Pennington, "The Development of Baroque Guitar Music in Spain," 1:302–3.

143. Murcia, *Resumen de acompañar,* 44. Cf. Valls, "Mapa armónico práctico," fol. 226r.

144. Murcia, *Resumen de acompañar,* 10–11. Cf. my discussion of that topic with Russell, "Santiago de Murcia: Spanish Theorist," 1:128–33, and Pennington, "The Development of Baroque Guitar Music in Spain," 1:274–81.

145. Andrés Lorente, *El porqué de la música* (Alcalá de Henares: Nicolás de Xamares, 1672), 562–66; Nasarre, *Fragmentos músicos,* 60–63; and *José de Torres's Treatise of 1736: General Rules for Accompanying on the Organ, Harpsichord, and the Harp,* ed. Paul Murphy (Bloomington and Indianapolis: Indiana University Press, 2000), 23–30.

146. Nasarre, *Fragmentos músicos,* 116.

147. See *Santiago de Murcia's "Códice Saldívar No. 4,"* 1:26–114, and Esses, *Dance and Instrumental Diferencias in Spain,* 1:599–753.

148. There were some exceptions. For example, "Las vacas" and "Los imposibles" share a unique harmonic scheme, so that the difference between them is essentially rhythmic; see *Santiago de Murcia's "Códice Saldívar No. 4,"* 1:45.

149. The problem of the concept of the work in music history has been widely treated by many scholars and obviously

exceeds the space and focus of the present study. For instance, I refer the reader to the classic book of Carl Dahlhaus, *Foundations of Music History*, trans. J. B. Robinson (Cambridge: Cambridge University Press, 1989), 33–43. Also of much interest are the reflections of Leo Treitler, *Music and the Historical Imagination* (Cambridge, Mass. and London: Harvard University Press, 1989), 30–36, 170–71, and so on.

150. Cited by Michael L. Klein, *Intertextuality in Western Art Music* (Bloomington and Indianapolis: Indiana University Press, 2005), 143.

151. The problems involved in distinguishing a written from an oral musical tradition in pure terms are called into question, for example, by Joseph Kerman, "A Few Canonic Variations," *Critical Inquiry* 10 (1983): 110–14.

152. Something that also occurs in the *pasacalles* and other dances of Guerau's *Poema harmonico*.

153. Pennington, "The Development of Baroque Guitar Music in Spain," 1:298–300. See also Russell, "Santiago de Murcia: Spanish Theorist," 1:221–24.

154. To indicate the register I follow the chart included in *NG2*, s.v. "Pitch nomenclature" (p. 806), by Llewelyn S. Lloyd and Richard Rastall.

155. *Santiago de Murcia's "Códice Saldívar No. 4,"* 1:12–16, and Esses, *Dance and Instrumental Diferencias in Spain*, 1:345–49.

156. Esses, *Dance and Instrumental Diferencias in Spain*, 1:352–53.

157. *Santiago de Murcia's "Códice Saldívar No. 4,"* 1:55–57, 94–95.

158. Esses, *Dance and Instrumental Diferencias in Spain*, 1:530.

159. The scarce references to these genres are quoted in *Santiago de Murcia's "Códice Saldívar No. 4,"* 1:45, 92–93; and Esses, *Dance and Instrumental Diferencias in Spain*, 1:667, 676–77.

160. *DRAE* (1729), 2:160, available at NTLLE (accessed 3 July 2008).

161. Robert Stevenson quoted the entry "corrido de la costa" in *Music in Aztec and Inca Territory* (1968; reprint, California: University of California Press, 1976), 235. The reference to Malaga, however, is not supplied there but in the entry "Costa," subentry "Corrido de la costa": "A certain strum that is commonly played on the guitar or another instrument, with which the *jácaras* are sung. It is called this because it was invented on the coast of Malaga." (Cierto tañido que se toca en la guitarra u otro instrumento, a cuyo son se cantan las que llaman jácaras. Díjose así, porque se inventó en la Costa de Málaga.) *DRAE* (1729), 2:640, available at NTLLE (accessed 15 July 2008).

162. Esses, *Dance and Instrumental Diferencias in Spain*, 1:352–53.

163. On the *españoletas* see *Santiago de Murcia's "Códice Saldívar No. 4,"* 1:34–35. On *paradetas* see Esses, *Dance and Instrumental Diferencias in Spain*, 1:683–84.

164. Esses, *Dance and Instrumental Diferencias in Spain*, 1:722–24.

165. See *DRAE* (1739), 6:532, available at NTLLE (accessed 15 July 2008). See also *Santiago de Murcia's "Códice Saldívar No. 4,"* 1:26–30, and Esses, *Dance and Instrumental Diferencias in Spain*, 1:668–73.

166. See a complete transcription, including its first section (*estribillo*), in Vera, *Música vocal profana*, 537–52.

167. See M. 1370, p. 97, E-Mn. I owe this concordance to Juan Jorquera.

168. Cf. Luis Antonio González Marín, "Recuperación o restauración del teatro musical español del siglo XVII," in *La ópera en España e Hispanoamérica*, 1:67.

169. On the function of this genre see Luis Robledo, *Juan Blas de Castro (ca. 1561–1631): Vida y obra musical* (Zaragoza: Institución Fernando el Católico, 1989), and Vera, *Música vocal profana*, 71–94.

170. See O'Dania, "The 'Academia Musical' of Pablo Minguet y Yrol," 23–24.

171. See Klein, *Intertextuality in Western Art Music*, 62.

172. See, among others, María Asunción Flórez, *Música teatral en el Madrid de los Austrias durante el Siglo de Oro* (Madrid: ICCMU, 2006), 207–14.

173. See Carmelo Caballero, *"Arded, corazón, arded": Tonos humanos del Barroco en la Península Ibérica* (Valladolid: Las Edades del Hombre, 1997), 153–55. I found this concordance through Stein, *Songs of Mortals*, 384. I am grateful to Susana Antón for drawing my attention to Caballero's edition.

174. M. 2478, E-Mn. This harp manuscript is undated, but it was probably copied in the late seventeenth or early eighteenth century. Stein, *Songs of Mortals*, 359, affirms that its later section was copied in 1709.

175. I am grateful to Antonio Corona for sending his own inventory of that source to me. Aside from this, there is a less complete but useful description in Stevenson, *Music in Aztec and Inca Territory*, 234–35. I have not been able to consult the study by Craig H. Russell, "New Jewels in Old Boxes: Retrieving the Lost Musical Heritages of Colonial Mexico," *Ars Musica Denver* 7, no. 2 (1995): 13–38. A general commentary on this source can be found in Tyler and Sparks, *The Guitar and Its Music*, 151.

176. *Santiago de Murcia's "Códice Saldívar No. 4,"* 1:95–96, 98. But, at the same time, it should be noted that the "Sarao" included in "Códice Saldívar" (fol. 71r) was not used in the *Sarao de la minué francés* as Russell has conjectured, since none of the pieces edited by Caballero correspond to it.

177. According to the abovementioned inventory (note 175) by the musicologist Antonio Corona.

178. This feature, among others, is mentioned by Coriún Aharonián in "Factores de identidad musical latinoamericana tras cinco siglos de conquista, dominación y mestizaje," *Latin American Music Review* 15 (1994): 199. A theoretic explanation about the *hemiola* in Spanish songs from the seventeenth century can be found in Vera, *Música vocal profana*, 145–46, and, with divergences, in Robledo, *Juan Blas de Castro*, 96–98.

179. Among the Hispanic genres cultivated by Murcia, the *fandango*, of which there is a version in "Códice Saldívar no. 4" (fol. 16r), is the only one whose presence in Chile has been documented for the eighteenth century. See Pereira Salas, *Los orígenes del arte musical en Chile*, 208.

180. *Santiago de Murcia's "Códice Saldívar No. 4,"* 1:107–8.

181. For examples of its cultivation there see Pereira Salas, *Los orígenes del arte musical en Chile*, 44, 70, 96, 156, 213, 230, 231, 255, and 256.

182. There is a minuet in ACS, folder 83, entitled "Minué del día 11 de marzo de 1767"; cf. Vera, "¿Decadencia o progreso?"

183. *Santiago de Murcia's "Códice Saldívar No. 4,"* 1:103.

184. Esses, *Dance and Instrumental Diferencias in Spain*, 1:684–91; Pennington, "The Development of Baroque Guitar Music in Spain," 1:293–95; Russell, "Santiago de Murcia: Spanish Theorist," 1:211–15.

185. Pennington, "The Development of Baroque Guitar Music in Spain," 1:304; Russell, "Santiago de Murcia: Spanish Theorist," 1:224.

186. On that topic, see *NG2*, s.v. "Notes inégales" (pp. 195–97), by David Fuller.

187. See Budasz, "The Five-course Guitar," 76–79, 96, and 338 (transcription). I have not been able to consult this source. Budasz does not provide concordances for this piece.

188. Russell, "Santiago de Murcia: Spanish Theorist," 1:146; Monica Hall, "Recovering a Lost Book of Guitar Music by Corbetta," *The Consort* 61 (2005): 3. This manuscript also attributes two *correntas* of "Passacalles y obras" to Corbetta (fols. 111v, 122v).

189. Hall, "Recovering a Lost Book," 9: "All the movements which make up the *obras*, or suites [in "Passacalles y obras"], are by other composers, although not all have yet been identified."

190. Hall herself stated in her dissertation that the *pasacalles* of "Passacalles y obras" were apparently original compositions by Murcia; see Hall, "The Guitar Anthologies," 1:i.

191. "Idea nueva, y obra especial de clarines" (fol. 45r [no. 53]), "Obra por la K3" (fol. 50v [no. 54]), and "Burée" (fol. 52v [no. 55]). For the first piece the title is taken from the list of contents.

192. M. 2478, E-Mn.

193. Lawrence Kramer, *Critical Musicology and the Responsibility of Response: Selected Essays* (Hampshire: Ashgate, 2006), xvi.

194. I do not mean that a historical analysis is opposed to semiotics or hermeneutics. A well-known example of a historicist semiotics is Robert S. Hatten, *Interpreting Musical Gestures, Topics, and Tropes: Mozart, Beethoven, Schubert* (Bloomington and Indianapolis: Indiana University Press, 2004), 33.

195. Cf. *Santiago de Murcia's "Códice Saldívar No. 4,"* 1:60, 164 and 2:33, 181.

196. For instance, see the suite movements included in "Obra por la C" (fol. 35v) and "Obra por la K3" (fol. 50v).

197. I understand topics (or *topoi*) as "signs that operate within a closed corpus and in a specifically delimited cultural and musical context"; see Kofi Agawu, "The Challenge of Semiotics," in *Rethinking Music,* ed. Nicholas Cook and Mark Everist (Oxford and New York: Oxford University Press, 2001), 156. Cf. Klein, *Intertextuality in Western Art Music,* 72.

198. Cf. *Santiago de Murcia's "Códice Saldívar No. 4,"* 1:38–39.

199. That is, highly marked musical events "that direct our attention to some aspect of the ongoing musical discourse," characterized by a sudden change and implying a "higher, narrative agency"; see Hatten, *Interpreting Musical Gestures, Topics, and Tropes,* 164–65.

200. "Meterse a caballero ... pretender ser o parecer uno más de lo que es: lo que comúnmente se dice de muchos, que por haber adquirido algunos medios, y con ellos elevar más la fortuna con que nacieron, se meten a hombrear con los hombres conocidos, y a querer parecer más entre los iguales." *DRAE* (1729), 2:8, available at NTLLE (accessed 20 July 2008).

201. *Santiago de Murcia's "Códice Saldívar No. 4,"* 1:38, and Esses, *Dance and Instrumental Diferencias in Spain,* 1:553.

202. "Villano ... Se toma asimismo por rústico, u descortés ... Significa también ruin, indigno, u indecoroso." *DRAE* (1739), 6:488, available at NTLLE (accessed 20 July 2008).

203. A "Villano caballero" is also found in Fernández de Huete's harp book, *Compendio numeroso* (1702), and the undated "Eleanor Hague manuscript"; see *Santiago de Murcia's "Códice Saldívar No. 4,"* 1:153.

204. See Morales, *L'Artiste de cour,* 129–65, and Esses, *Dance and Instrumental Diferencias in Spain,* 1:36–43.

205. See, among others, Juan José Carreras, "From Literes to Nebra: Spanish Dramatic Music between Tradition and Modernity," in *Music in Spain during the Eighteenth Century,* ed. Malcom Boyd and Juan José Carreras (Cambridge: Cambridge University Press, 1998), 7–16.

206. See Álvaro Torrente, "Italianate Sections in the Villancicos of the Royal Chapel, 1700–1740," in *Music in Spain during the Eighteenth Century,* 72–79. See also Torrente, "The Sacred Villancico," 1:101–16.

207. As stated by Russell, "Santiago de Murcia: Spanish Theorist," 1:259.

208. The term *clarín* designated at that time a folded trumpet commonly pitched in D or C. See *NG2,* s.v. "Clarín (1)" (p. 895), by Beryl Kenyon de Pascual.

209. This fact was already noted by the authors of the *Catalogue of Manuscript Music in the British Museum* (London: Trustees of the British Museum, 1965), 3:55, who state: "The suite which commences at f. 58 is described as 'Una Ydea Especial de Clarines' (? = trumpet tunes), and includes a long Prelude, 'Canciones,' 'Llamadas' (? = trumpet calls), Marcha, 'Fagina,' and 'Menuet de Clarin.'" This description was cited by Pennington, "The Development of Baroque Guitar Music in Spain," 1:273, who, in spite of this, considered these pieces as additional Spanish dances to a previous suite in the same key (p. 309). The same criterion was adopted by Hall, "The Guitar Anthologies," 1:491. On the contrary, its status as a suite was noted by Company; see *Suites del libro "Passacalles y obras,"* 20–30.

210. Cf. Pennington, "The Development of Baroque Guitar Music in Spain," 1:315, and Russell, "Santiago de Murcia: Spanish Theorist," 1:260.

211. Russell, "Santiago de Murcia: Spanish Theorist," 1:263–64. Cf. Russell and Topp Russell, "El arte de recomposición," 11–13. The concordant pieces are: "Idea nueva ..." (only fragments), "Marcha," "Canción de ecos," and "Fajina." The "Canción" can be seen in a recent edition: *Flores de música: Obras y versos de varios organistas escriptas por Fray Antonio Martín Coll,* ed. Genoveva Gálvez (Madrid: Fidelio Música, 2007), 25, 49, 104.

212. "Toque que ordena la retirada de las tropas a sus alojamientos o el término de una facción." This definition, cited by Russell and Pennington, only appears in the dictionary of the *Real Academia Española* from 1925 on. Before this, the first edition defining *fajina* as a military call dates from 1817. Nonetheless, "Cifras selectas" suggests that it already had that meaning about 1722.

213. According to Antonio Corona's inventory. Cf. Stevenson, *Music in Aztec and Inca Territory,* 235. There has been some speculation on the possible links between these *valonas* and the traditional song performed in Mexico today, in spite of their very different content from a musical point of view; see Fernando Nava, "Décima. V. México," and Thomas Stanford, "México. V. Música popular indígena," in *DMEH,* 4:430 and 7:522, respectively.

214. See Fernando Redondo Díaz, "El ejército," in *La España de las reformas: Hasta el final del reinado de Carlos IV,* vol. 10, pt. 2 of *Historia general de España y América* (Madrid: Rialp, 1984), 165. In about 1750 its headquarters was placed in a house owned by the king in Madrid; see *Libro primero de los asientos de las casas de Madrid,* 265. There is a "Marcha de las guardias valonas" in a manuscript entitled "Libro de la ordenanza de los toques de pífanos y tambores que se tocan nuevamente en la infantería española" (1761), M. 2791, fol. 8v, E-Mn. However, from a musical point of view it has nothing to do with the "Marcha valona" included in "Cifras selectas de guitarra."

215. The definition of the word *carabinero* has been taken from *DRAE* (1729), 2:159, available at NTLLE (accessed 17 July 2008).

216. See, respectively, Redondo Díaz, "El ejército," 156, 165, and Fernando Tejedo-Herrero and Francisco Gago-Jover, "El Diccionario militar de Raimundo Sanz en el contexto de la lexicografía especializada del siglo XVIII," *Dieciocho* 29 (2006): 87. I am grateful to Dr. Tejedo-Herrero for sending this article to me.

217. This march shows the common traits associated with the genre, such as repeated rhythms and even an initial fanfare; see *NG2,* s.v. "March" (pp. 812–18), by Erich Schwandt and Andrew Lamb.

218. A third candidate, though less probable, might be Marie Anna of Austria, Philip IV's second wife and Charles II's mother, who died in 1696.

219. See Henry Kamen, *La guerra de sucesión en España, 1700–1715,* trans. Enrique de Obregón (Barcelona: Grijalbo S. A., 1974), 19–34. The reader can consult the original edition in English: *The War of Succession in Spain, 1700–1715* (London: Weidenfeld and Nicolson, 1969). See also Carlos Fisas, *Historia de las reinas de España* (Barcelona: Planeta, 1988), 1:169–71.

220. Morales, *L'Artiste de cour,* 317.

221. Everett W. Hesse, "Courtly Allusions in the Plays of Calderón," *PMLA* 65 (1950): 547; and Margaret Rich Greer, "Art and Power in the Spectacle Plays of Calderón de la Barca," *PMLA* 104 (1989): 335.

222. "Parid, bella flor de lis / que en aflicción tan extraña / si parís, parís a España / si no parís, a París"; cited by Fisas, *Historia de las reinas de España,* 155. These verses hinted at the need for a crown prince who would never arrive.

223. See Klein, *Intertextuality in Western Art Music,* 1–21.

224. On this point I follow the pioneering article by Robert S. Hatten, "The Place of Intertextuality in Music Studies," *American Journal of Semiotics* 3, no. 4 (1985): 69–82.

225. Compare, for instance, my own table of concordances in "Santiago de Murcia's *Cifras Selectas de Guitarra,*" 258–61, to that of the present edition.

226. François Campion, *Nouvelles découvertes sur la guitarre* (1705; facsimile edition, with an introduction by François Lesure, Geneva: Minkoff Reprint, 1977), 50–51, 56–57. All the references to this source come from this edition.

227. For the concordances of "Passacalles y obras," see Hall, "The Guitar Anthologies," 1:489–507; Russell, "Santiago de Murcia: Spanish Theorist," 1:236–53; and Russell and Topp Russell, "El arte de recomposición," 15–18.

228. Castillion, "Recueil des pièces de guitarre," 10.

229. See *NG2*, s.v. "Martín y Coll, Antonio" (p. 1), by Barton Hudson. See also the recent edition by Gálvez, *Flores de música*, quoted above. The original manuscripts, which I have not consulted yet, are preserved as M. 1357–60, E-Mn.

230. Hall, "The Guitar Anthologies," 1:63.

231. Morales, *L'Artiste de cour*, 150–51.

232. "Et à la fin du siècle dernier, et au commencement du présent j'ai encore vu que la guitare étoit seule à la mode, et que Madame l'Électrice de Bavière se faisoit enseigner par le Sr. François Le Cocq." Castillion, "Recueil des pièces de guitarre," Préface.

233. I raised this alternative for the first time in "Santiago de Murcia's *Cifras Selectas de Guitarra*," 262–63.

234. Monica Hall, "Santiago de Murcia versus François Le Cocq" (correspondence), *Early Music* 35 (2007): 687.

235. This concordance was identified in Robert de Visée, *Les deux livres de guitarre: Paris 1682 et 1686*, ed. Hélène Charnassé, Rafael Andia, and Gérard Rebours (Paris: Éditions Transatlantiques, 1999), 89, 205–6. Possibly a detailed study of concordances of the "Recueil" would allow for an identification of more pieces taken from other sources.

236. Morales, *L'Artiste de cour*, 184–85.

237. See, among others, Tyler and Sparks, *The Guitar and Its Music*, 160; Russell and Topp Russell, "El arte de recomposición," 5; and Lolo, *La música en la Real Capilla de Madrid*, 56.

238. Hall, "Recovering a Lost Book," 6–8.

239. I share this point with Hall, "The Guitar Anthologies," 1:353.

240. "Menuet fácil," "Marsellas por la B," "Paspied nuevo," and very possibly also the "Paspied viejo" (which is entirely lost as fol. 42 is missing).

241. Not six, as I indicated, erroneously, in "Santiago de Murcia's *Cifras Selectas de Guitarra*," 257. These and other similar procedures have been studied for other sources in Russell and Topp Russell, "El arte de recomposición," 7–11.

242. See Sanz, *Instrucción de música*, cvi. The transcription of both variations can be seen in Vera, "Santiago de Murcia's *Cifras Selectas de Guitarra*," 264.

243. Before this passage there is another concordant variation, though the similitude is less evident.

244. The chaconne is attributed to Corbetta in two other manuscripts; see Hall, "Recovering a Lost Book," 3. The concordances between "Passacalles y obras" and Corbetta can be seen in Hall, "The Guitar Anthologies," 1:501, 507.

245. John P. Murphy, "Jazz Improvisation: The Joy of Influence," *The Black Perspective in Music* 18 (1990): 9–13.

246. Ingrid Monson, "Doubleness and Jazz Improvisation: Irony, Parody, and Ethnomusicology," *Critical Inquiry* 20 (1994): 303.

247. "And there are little dots near each number in order to keep the appropriate order of fingers . . ." (Y, para llevar los dedos bien ordenados, se ponen los puntillos junto al número . . .) Murcia, "Cifras selectas de guitarra," Explicación.

248. "One of the most important issues to be observed by whoever accompanies or plays is the good order of the left hand." (Pues es una de las mayores observaciones que debe observar el que acompaña o tañe, que es la buena ordenación de la mano izquierda.) Murcia, *Resumen de acompañar*, 8.

249. See Pennington, "The Development of Baroque Guitar Music in Spain," 1:336, and Russell, "Santiago de Murcia: Spanish Theorist," 2:xi–xii.

250. Russell, "Santiago de Murcia: Spanish Theorist," 2:xi.

251. Cf. ibid., xiii–xiv.

252. *The Baroque Guitar in Spain*, 23.

253. "And the hand only rested on the bridge when it is required for it to sound louder, as when accompanying another instrument." (Y solo usar de la mano puesta en la puentecilla cuando se necesita que suene más, como cuando se acompaña a otro instrumento.) Murcia, "Cifras selectas de guitarra," Explicación.

254. Sanz, *Instrucción de música*, lxxi: ". . . aplicando, si fuere necesario, el cuarto dedo de la mano drecha [*sic*] para la cuarta voz, en algunos puntos." See also Guerau, *Poema harmonico*, 11, 27, 28.

255. The only exception I have been able to find is in "Pasacalles de compasillo por la D," measure 2 (fol. 62r), which includes a four-part chord in plucked style.

256. Murcia, *Resumen de acompañar*, 10, 15, 45, 50, 54.

257. "If you play from the bass strings upwards, it must be with the thumb up to the second string; and from there up with the index and middle finger." (Y si glosas de los bordones hacia arriba, ha de ser con el pulgar hasta la segunda; y de ella arriba con el índice y largo.) Guerau, *Poema harmonico*, 5.

258. "Noticing that the thumb is used for the thirds, fourths, and fifths [strings]; the other two [index and middle fingers], for the seconds and firsts; taking great care to avoid plucking twice with the same finger, for the index and middle fingers have to pluck alternately." (Advirtiendo que el pulgar sirve para terceras, cuartas y quintas; los otros dos, para segundas y primas; con el cuidado que nunca se hiere dos veces con un mismo dedo, pues siempre índice y el del corazón han de herir alternativamente.) Murcia, "Cifras selectas de guitarra," Explicación. The mention of the "firsts" in plural has some interest, since it suggests that Murcia used two strings in the first course, unlike the prevailing practice among contemporary baroque guitarists.

259. *Santiago de Murcia's "Códice Saldívar No. 4,"* 2:xiv. A combination of both kinds of trills was also defended by Pennington, "The Development of Baroque Guitar Music in Spain," 1:323.

260. Robert Strizich, "Ornamentation in Spanish Baroque Guitar Music," *Journal of the Lute Society of America* 5 (1972): 27.

261. "Siendo siempre el trinado en el traste de adonde se levanta el dedo." Murcia, "Cifras selectas de guitarra," Explicación.

262. "Lo explicado podrá conducir a dar algún conocimiento para ejecutar las gracias y feligranas que caben en este instrumento (como único), las cuales son el alma de lo que se tañe; pero, no obstante, no podrá el aficionado de buen gusto, y no perezoso, sacar el fruto como de oírlas ejecutar al diestro, que con la voz viva pueda dirigir con fundamentales principios; no aquellos congregados en el número de aporriantes, o variadores de bellota, que pretenden saborar el sentido del oído a fuerza de andar a puñadas con la guitarra. Dios nos libre de tal granizo de verano." Murcia, "Cifras selectas de guitarra," Explicación.

263. See Pepe Rey, "Guitarra. I. España. 2. La guitarra de cinco órdenes," in *DMEH*, 6:95–96.

264. Obviously, this viewpoint is not the only one to be taken into account by a performer. But, if the construction of music history is actually a dialogue between past and present, a historical performance undoubtedly involves the same elements, as has been defended, among others, by Leo Treitler, "History and Music," *New Literary History* 21 (1990): 299–319.

Transcription and Translation of the Preliminary Texts

The preliminary texts are transcribed according to the same policies adopted for historical documents quoted in the introduction, i.e., with spelling modernized when it has no phonetic value, and with accents and punctuation modernized as well.

[Apuntes elementales de teoría musical]

Ut – Re – Mi – Fa – Sol – La –
GSolreu – Alamire – Bfami – CSolfau – Dlasolre – Elami – Ffaut.

En tiempo de compasillo, vale el breve dos compases;
el semibreve un compás;
dos mínimas un compás;
cuatro semínimas un compás;
~~diez y seis~~ – ocho corcheas un compás;
diez y seis semicorcheas un compás.

[Elementary notes on music theory]

Ut – Re – Mi – Fa – Sol – La –
GSolreu – Alamire – Bfami – CSolfau – Dlasolre – Elami – Ffaut.

In common time, the breve is two measures long;
the whole note, one measure;
two half notes, one measure;
four quarter notes, one measure;
~~sixteen~~ – eight eighth notes, one measure;
sixteen sixteenth notes, one measure.

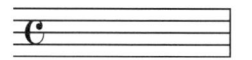

Clave de CSolfau
CSolfau clef
espacio   space
líneas   lines

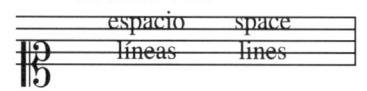

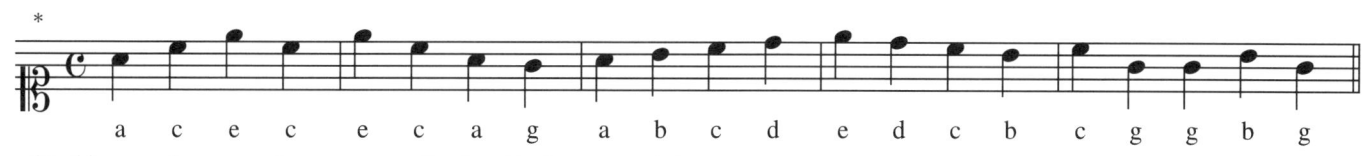

breve –   semibreve –   mínima –   semínima –   corchea –   semicorchea
breve –   whole note – half note – quarter note – eighth note – sixteenth note

a c e c e c a g a b c d e d c b c g g b g

*In this example, some notes are incorrectly placed in the manuscript.

[Instrucciones para afinar la guitarra en relación con otros instrumentos]

Para templar la guitarra, digo ponerla con arpa, se igualan las [terceras] toca[das] al aire con el quinto bordón del arpa.

Para templar la guitarra con bandurria se igualan las terceras al aire con las segundas de la bandurria, pisadas éstas en segundo traste; y estas mismas se igualan así con el quinto bordón del arpa.

Para poner la guitarra con violín se igualan las terceras de la guitarra pisadas en segundo traste con la segunda del violín.

Para poner acordes guitarra, bandurria y violín se igualan la prima de la guitarra con la prima del violín y con la segunda de la bandurria; o si no, mejor es igualar las terceras de la guitarra pisadas en 2 traste con la segunda del violín; y se templan las demás cuerdas de la guitarra; y después de bien templada, se hace el segundo punto natural y se tañe un poco, y si los 3 instrumentos no hacen una voz, el del violín puede ir igualando su segunda y el de la bandurria su prima, porque son más fáciles de templar.

Para templar la guitarra con el tiple, se igualan las terceras del tiple con las cuartas de la guitarra, de suerte que hagan una misma voz, y las demás se templan, ni más ni menos, como las de la guitarra.

Para templar el violín con la guitarra se iguala la quinta de la guitarra al aire, que es Alamire, con la segunda del violín en la misma consonancia, y las otras cuerdas del violín se templan al tenor de la segunda; y, templadas guitarra y violín, quedan las cuerdas de uno y otro consonantes como se sigue, vg. =

*Notes 1 and 3 are incorrectly placed in the manuscript.

Para templar la guitarra con el violín, se toca el bordón del violín suelto y se ponen las terceras de la guitarra en la misma consonancia que hace el bordón, vg.:

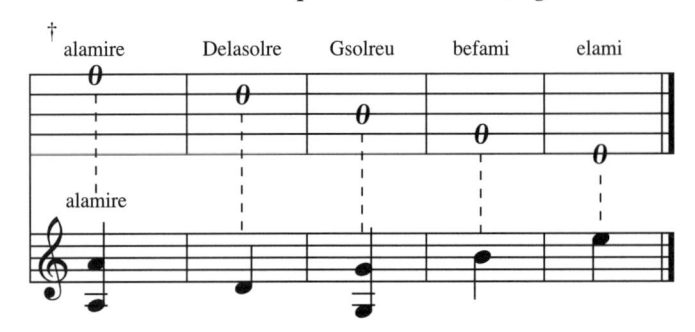

†In measure 1, the clef and lower note are incorrectly placed in the manuscript.

[Instructions for tuning the guitar in relation to other instruments]

For tuning the guitar, or rather for matching it with the harp, equalize the open [third strings] with the fifth bourdon of the harp.

For tuning the guitar with the bandurria, equalize the open third strings with the second strings of the bandurria, stopped on the second fret; then, equalize these strings with the fifth bourdon of the harp.

For tuning the guitar with the violin, equalize the third strings of the guitar stopped on the second fret with the second string of the violin.

In order to tune the guitar, bandurria, and violin, equalize the first string of the guitar with the first string of the violin and the second string of the bandurria; otherwise, it is better to match the third strings of the guitar stopped on the second fret with the second string of the violin; and the remaining guitar strings are tuned; and once it is well tuned, prepare the second major chord and play it a little, and if the three instruments do not sound as one voice, the violinist can adjust his second string and the bandurria player his first string, because their instruments are easier to tune.

For tuning the guitar with the tiple, equalize the third strings of the tiple with the fourth strings of the guitar, so that they sound as a single voice, and the rest are tuned, no more and no less, as those of the guitar.

For tuning the violin with the guitar, equalize the open fifth string of the guitar, which is Alamire, with the second string of the violin in the same pitch, and tune the remaining strings of the violin according to the second; and once the guitar and violin are tuned, the strings of both instruments must be pitched as follows, viz. =

For tuning the guitar with the violin, play the open bourdon of the violin and match the third strings of the guitar with the same pitch as that of the bourdon, viz.:

Explicación para facilitar la ejecución en aquellas cosas más estrañas de estas obras

Suponiendo la inteligencia en sacar la cifra, la cual es que las cinco líneas son las cinco cuerdas de la guitarra, comenzando a contar desde la ínfima, que es la prima, y así hasta la última, que es la quinta; los números que se hallan en dichas líneas o cuerdas (que es lo mismo) son los trastes en donde se ha de pisar: si fuere un uno en primero traste; si un dos, en segundo; si un tres, en tercero; y así de los demás. Donde se halla un cero se herirá aquella cuerda en vacío sin pisar en ningún traste. Cuando están los números unos encima de otros, se herirán a un tiempo. Esto es en cuanto a la mano izquierda, y, para llevar los dedos bien ordenados, se ponen los puntillos junto al número, que siendo uno se pisará con el dedo índice; si fueren dos punticos, se pisará con el dedo del corazón; si fuesen tres, con el anular; si fuesen cuatro, con el meñique; cuya dirección se pone en todos los tañidos inclusivamente hasta el folio 26, persuadido que, enterado del práctico conocimiento de lo expresado, podrá el aficionado curioso servirle de luz y conocimiento para el residuo de las restantes obras de este libro, y de todas las demás. Tocante a la mano derecha, en primer lugar se advierte que el común estilo a todos los principiantes es que pongan el dedo meñique fuera de la puente de la guitarra, para que esté más firme la mano, porque muchos no pueden entonces herir las cuerdas puesta la mano en el aire, sino de la suerte dicha; lo cual no se verá practicado en ningún diestro, que trate a este instrumento con algún primor, mayormente cuando son obras delicadas y en ellas hay golpes rasgueados, pues debe en estos casos tocarse en el medio del instrumento, y solo usar de la mano puesta en la puentecilla cuando se necesita que suene más, como cuando se acompaña a otro instrumento. Los dedos con que se hieren las cuerdas son el pulgar, el índice y el del corazón; advirtiendo que el pulgar sirve para terceras, cuartas y quintas; los otros dos, para segundas y primas; con el cuidado que nunca se hiere dos veces con un mismo dedo, pues siempre índice y el del corazón han de herir alternativamente. Esto es en cuanto a sacar la cifra llana, pues para otras gracias, que van señaladas en estas obras, y así mesmo el modo de ordenar la mano en la precisa ejecución de muchas cosas dificultosas, se explicarán todas con sus ejemplos. Primeramente, siempre que se hallase una raya que atraviesa las líneas, y que los números estén uno después de otro, se considerará uno encima de otro, como si fuera golpe lleno, herido a un tiempo, que por lo regular es en tres cuerdas; cuyo ejemplo se verá en las Jácaras de la E, en el primero folio, a la vuelta de la hoja, últimas diferencias, vg.

Explanation to facilitate the execution of the strangest things in these works

Assuming the reader knows how to interpret the tablature, in which five lines represent the five strings of the guitar, beginning to count from the lower string, which is the first, up to the last, which is the fifth; the numbers in these lines or strings (which is the same) represent the frets to be stopped: with number one, the first fret; with number two, the second; with number three, the third; and so on. Where there is a zero, that string must be plucked without stopping any fret. When the numbers are placed on top of each other, they must be plucked at the same time. All of this concerns the left hand, and there are little dots near each number in order to keep the appropriate order of fingers, one dot meaning that the fret must be stopped with the index finger; two dots, with the middle finger; three, with the ring finger; four, with the little finger; which are indicated in each piece until folio 26 inclusive, on the belief that this practical knowledge will orient the eager amateur in the remaining pieces of this book, and others. As for the right hand, first, the common style for all beginners is that they put the little finger near the bridge of the guitar, so that the hand will be firmer, and thus many cannot pluck the strings as the hand is in the air, but in the abovementioned way; which will not be seen in anyone accomplished who deals with this instrument with some exquisiteness, especially when the pieces are delicate and include strummed strokes, as in these cases the instrument must be played in the middle and the hand only rested on the bridge when it is required for it to sound louder, as when accompanying another instrument. The fingers with which the strings are plucked are the thumb, index, and that of the ring; noticing that the thumb is used for the thirds, fourths, and fifths [strings]; the other two [index and middle fingers] for the seconds and firsts; taking great care to avoid plucking twice with the same finger, for the index and middle fingers have to pluck alternately. This is what can be said about the elementary symbols, but other graces indicated in these works, as well as the appropriate order of the [left] hand for an accurate performance of many difficult things, will be explained with their examples. First, when a line across the staff spans consecutive numbers, these must be stopped [by the left hand] on top of each other, as though it were a strummed stroke, played at the same time; this commonly involves three strings, just as in Jácaras por la E, turning the first folio, in the last variations, viz.

Este modo dicho se halla también con otra raya debajo, demás de la que atraviesa las líneas, la cual precisa a poner ceja, que es tender el dedo índice que comprenda todas las cuerdas por igual, sujetándolas con fuerza; advirtiendo que todas las veces que se hallase dicha raya se pondrá la ceja en el traste del número más ínfimo de los que señala la cifra, como se ve en el folio 18, en la última difrencia de folías, vg.

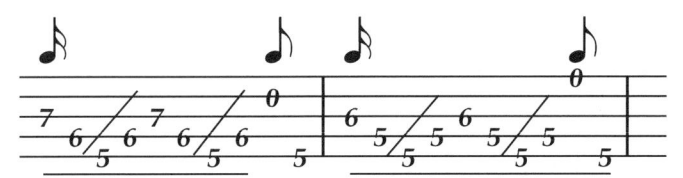

This symbol is also found with another line below, besides that through the staff, indicating a *bar*, that is, the index finger spanning the strings and pressing them tightly; noticing that whenever this line is found the *bar* must be placed in the lower number indicated in the staff, as seen on folio 18, in the last variation of the *folías*, viz.

También sirve esta raya para mantenerse en aquel traste todo el tiempo de la cifra que señala, como se verá en muchas partes. Los medios círculos que se hallan en la cifra se llaman extrasinos. La ejecución de éstos es herir el primero golpe o número desde adonde comienza el extrasino, y los demás que comprende los explica la mano izquierda; con la circunstancia que cuando van descendiendo de menos a más van cayendo los dedos; cuando empiezan de más a menos, se va rebatiendo hasta encontrar el más ínfimo número; siendo el mismo extrasino quien también lo explica, pues cuando está de la parte de arriba, y los números debajo, es cayendo los dedos; cuando están los números encima, y el extrasino debajo, es ir rebatiendo como queda dicho;* siendo ejemplo de esto la última difrencia de la Jácara por la E, en el folio 2.

This line also implies to remain on that fret as long as indicated, as seen in many other parts. The half circles are called slurs. Their execution consists of plucking the first number where the slur begins, playing the others with the left hand; noticing that when the numbers drop [sic] from low to high the fingers are falling; when the numbers go from high to low, the fingers are retracting until the lower number; and this is shown by the slur itself, for when it is above the numbers the fingers are falling, and when the numbers are above it the fingers are retracting as explained,* what can be seen in the last variation of Jácara por la E, in folio 2.

*Murcia is mistaken on this point. Both the example and the pieces in the manuscript show exactly the opposite practice.

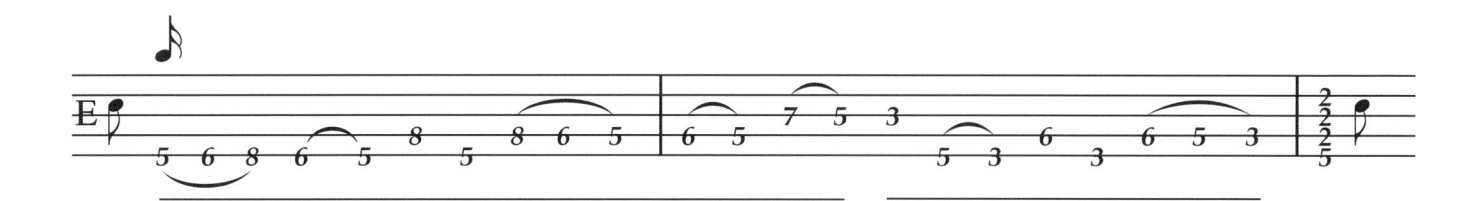

También suelen comenzar los extrasinos con el mismo golpe rasgueado, rebatiendo o cayendo según la regla dicha, como en el folio 77 al tercer compás del Preludio Grave de Coreli se ve, vg.

Frequently, the slurs begin with a strummed stroke, retracting or dropping fingers according to the abovementioned rule, as seen in folio 77 in the third measure of Preludio Grave of Corelli, viz.

Cuando es en dos cuerdas a un tiempo dicho extrasino, se advertirá que, siendo de más a menos, se se [sic] ha de tener prevenida la mano adonde va a parar, para que,

When the slur takes place simultaneously in two strings and it goes from high to low, keep in mind to prepare the position of the [left] hand where the slur is going to

rebatiendo ambos dedos a un tiempo, expliquen con claridad y limpieza adonde salen, vg.

de menos a más
from low to high

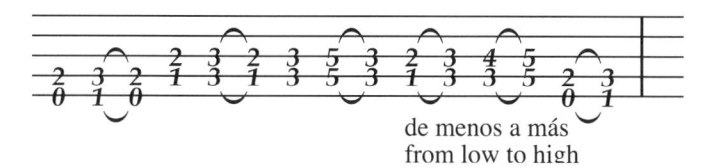

Al fin de todas las más tocadas o canciones, se hallan estos extrasinos con una señal al último como una coma, vg. , , la cual se llama mordente; su ejecución es: después de haber caído el dedo donde cierra el extrasino, se vuelve a rebatir dejándole caer con toda presteza, sin perder el tiempo, vg.

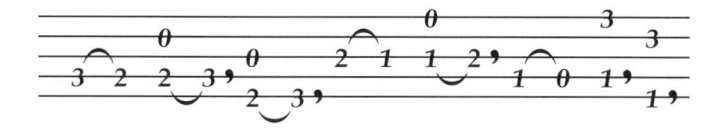

También esta señal del mordente se halla sin extrasino. Su ejecución será de la misma manera arriba dicha, siendo el rebatir y caer unas veces del traste antecedente y otras de dos trastes antes, según el tono por donde se tañe, y el buen oído del tañedor. Otras veces la misma cifra da el gobierno, vg.

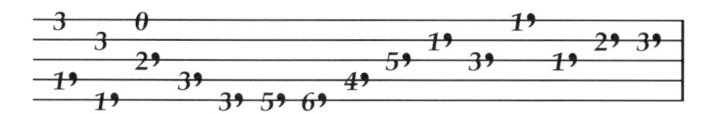

Esta señal ⁒ ⁒ que es la más común se llama trinado. Su ejecución es como quien araña aquella cuerda, siendo siempre el trinado en el traste de adonde se levanta el dedo; y cuando hubiere duda se atenderá si debajo del dicho trinado hay algún número pequeño, pues adonde se debe trinar, según fuere, vg.

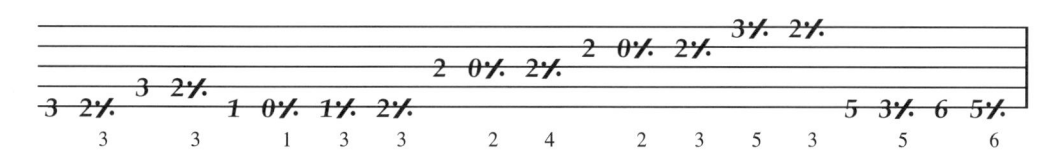

También se hallan en algunas ocasiones trinados en dos cuerdas a un tiempo. Para ejecutarlos, es necesario trinar con los dedos que se levantan de los trastes antecedentes, y trinar en los mismos trastes que se dejan, vg.

stop, in such a way that, retracting both fingers at the same time, they explain with clarity and cleanliness where they are going, viz.

At the end of most toccatas or songs, these slurs are ended with a comma, viz. , , which is called a mordent. Its execution is: after the finger has dropped where the slur ends, it is retracted again, then dropping it very fast, without wasting time, viz.

The mordent is also found without a slur. Its execution will be the same as explained above, retracting and dropping fingers sometimes from the previous fret, others from two frets before, depending on the key and the good ear of the performer. Sometimes the symbols on the staff show the appropriate way, viz.

This ⁒ ⁒ is the most common sign and it is called trill. Its execution is as though one scratches the string, the trill being always on the fret where the finger is lifted; and if the fret is not clear, see the little number below the trill, since it indicates the place for its execution, viz.

Sometimes, there are also trills on two strings at the same time. In order to perform them, it is necessary to lift the fingers from the previous frets, and then trill again on these same frets, viz.

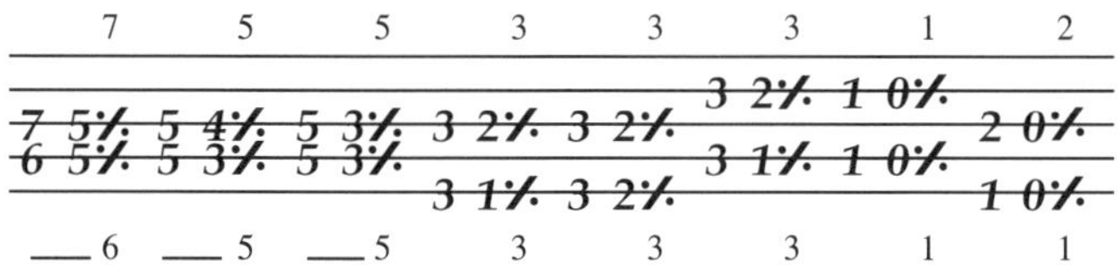

Lo explicado podrá conducir a dar algún conocimiento para ejecutar las gracias y feligranas que caben en este instrumento (como único), las cuales son el alma de lo que se tañe; pero, no obstante, no podrá el aficionado de buen gusto, y no perezoso, sacar el fruto como de oírlas ejecutar al diestro, que con la voz viva pueda dirigir con fundamentales principios; no aquellos congregados en el número de aporriantes, o variadores de bellota, que pretenden saborar el sentido del oído a fuerza de andar a puñadas con la guitarra. Dios nos libre de tal granizo de verano. En cuanto a dar el aire a lo que se tañe, también es dificultoso si no se oye o se sabe música, pues siendo sus mismos caracteres o figuras quien gobierna la cifra; solo diré, de paso, que esta figura o, que se llama semibreve, se halla al fin de las tocadas, la cual vale 1 compás; ésta ♩, que se llama mínima, los golpes que gobierna van despacio, por entrar dos al compás; ésta ♩ se llama semínima: se llevan más aprisa que la mínima, porque entran 4 al compás; ésta ♪ se llama corchea: va duplicado lo prompto de la semínima, porque entran 8 al compás; ésta ♪ se llama semicorchea: se toca otro más rápido que la corchea, porque entran 16 al compás. A cualquiera de esta figura que se halla con puntillo se le aumenta la mitad de su valor, vg. ♩. ♩. ♪. ♪.

This explanation may give some knowledge as to executing the graces and ornaments of this instrument (as unique), which constitute the soul of the performance; but, notwithstanding, it would be impossible for the amateur with good taste, and who is not lazy, to take as much advantage from it as from listening to an expert performing them, who can verbally instruct him in the fundamental principles; unlike those congregated among the number of punchers or acorn pickers who try to stimulate the sense of hearing by hitting the guitar. God save us from this summer hail. As for giving the appropriate character to the performed piece, it is also difficult if one does not know music, since its symbols or signs govern the staff. I will only say in passing that this figure o, called a whole note, is found at the end of the toccatas, and is 1 measure long; this ♩, called a half note, implies slow strokes, since two fit one measure; this ♩ is called a quarter note: it is kept faster than the half note, since 4 fit one measure; this ♪ is called an eighth note: its speed doubles that of the quarter note, since 8 fit one measure; this ♪ is called a sixteenth note: it is performed faster than the eighth note, since 16 fit one measure. Any figure of these with a dot increases its length by half, viz. ♩. ♩. ♪. ♪.

Transcription of the Music

1. Jácaras por la E

2. Marionas por la B

13

3. Difrencias de gallardas por la E

Fols. 3v–4v

4. Pavanas por la E

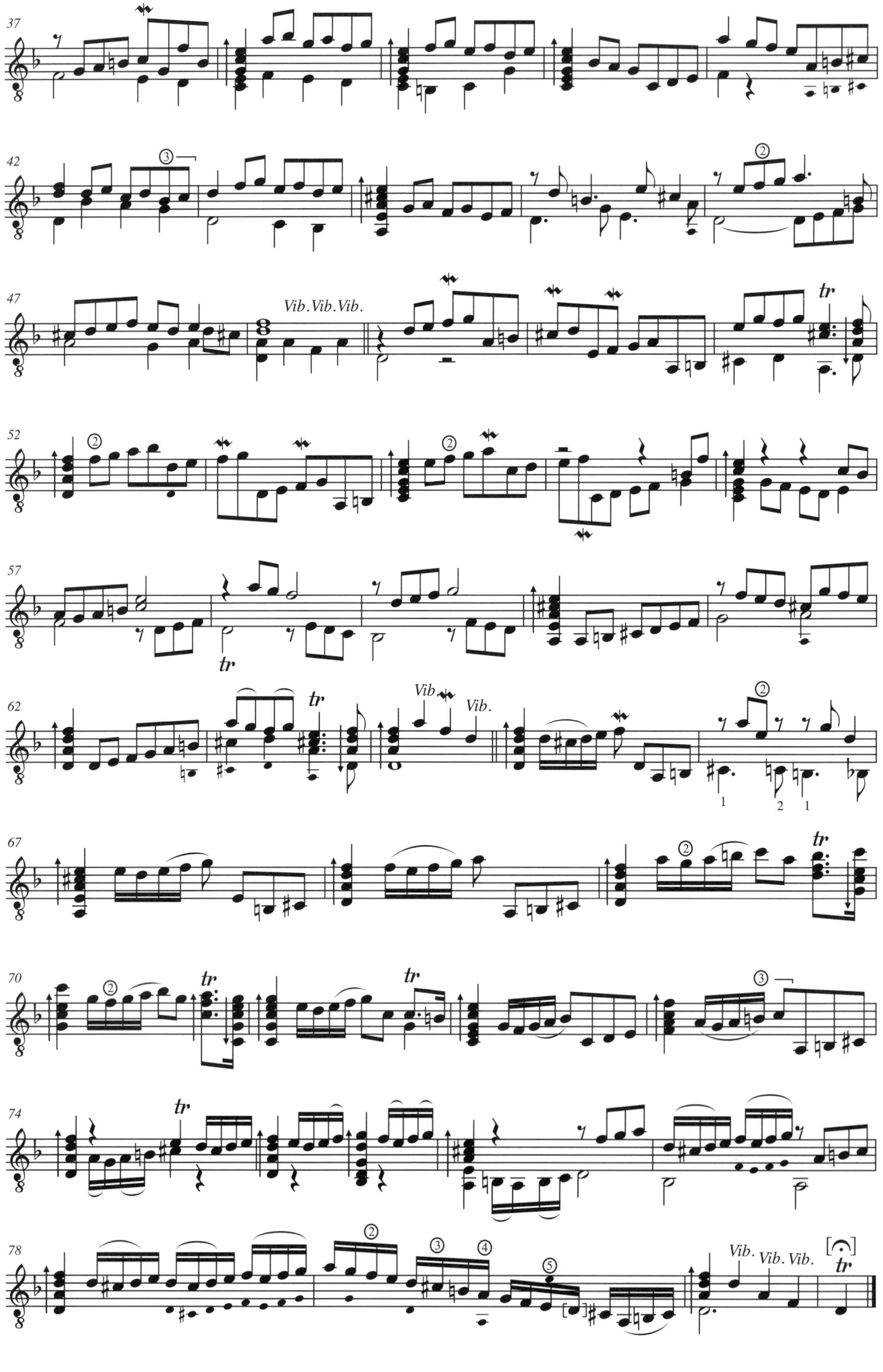
Vib. Vib. Vib.
Vib.
Vib.
Vib.
Vib. Vib. Vib.

5. Españoletas por la E

6. Folías españolas por la E

Fols. 7v–8v

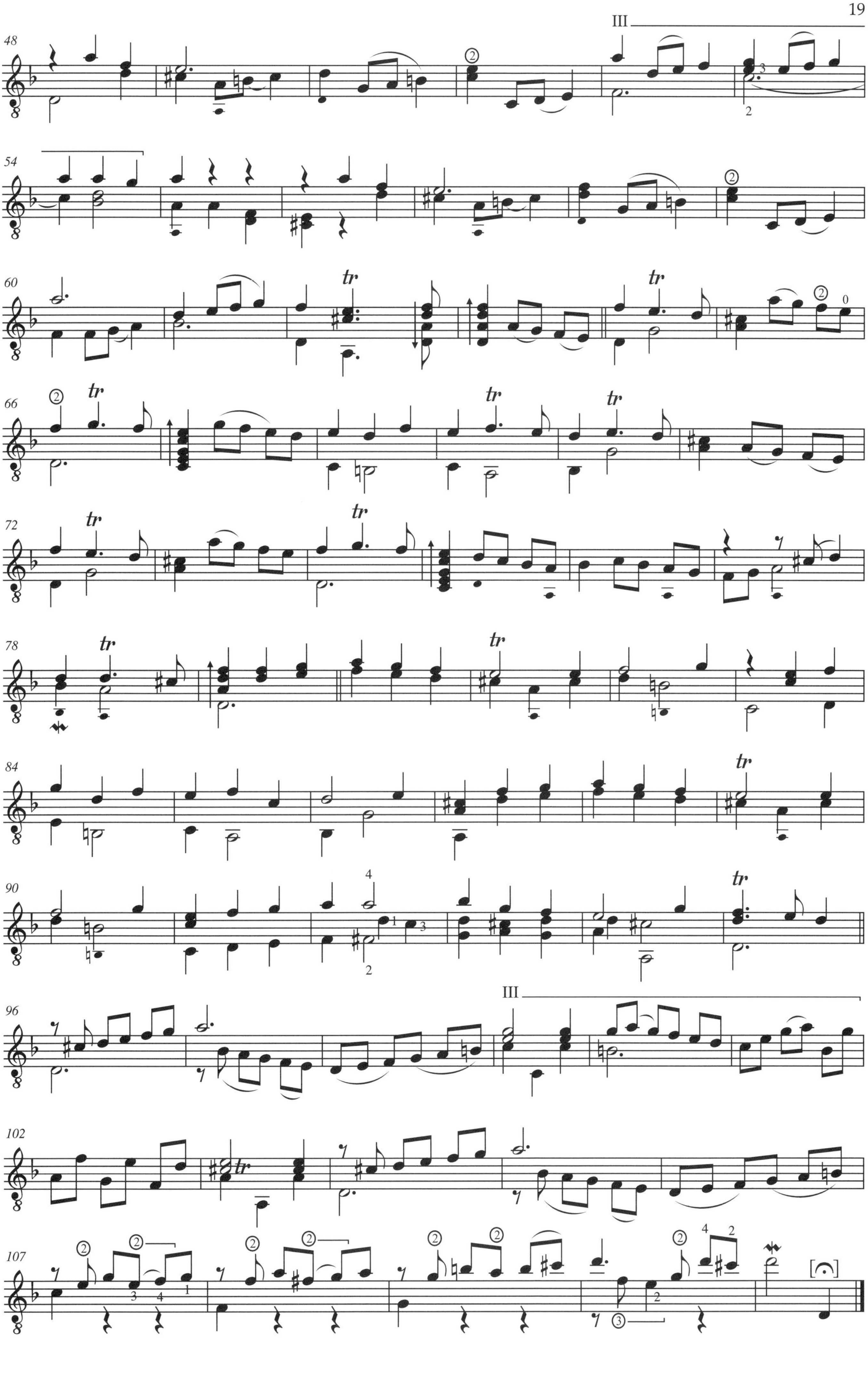
III
48
54
60
tr
66
72
78
84
90
96
102
107

7. Jácaras francesas por la D

Fols. 8v–9v

8. El Amor por la E

9. Tarantelas por la E

10. Las vacas por la E

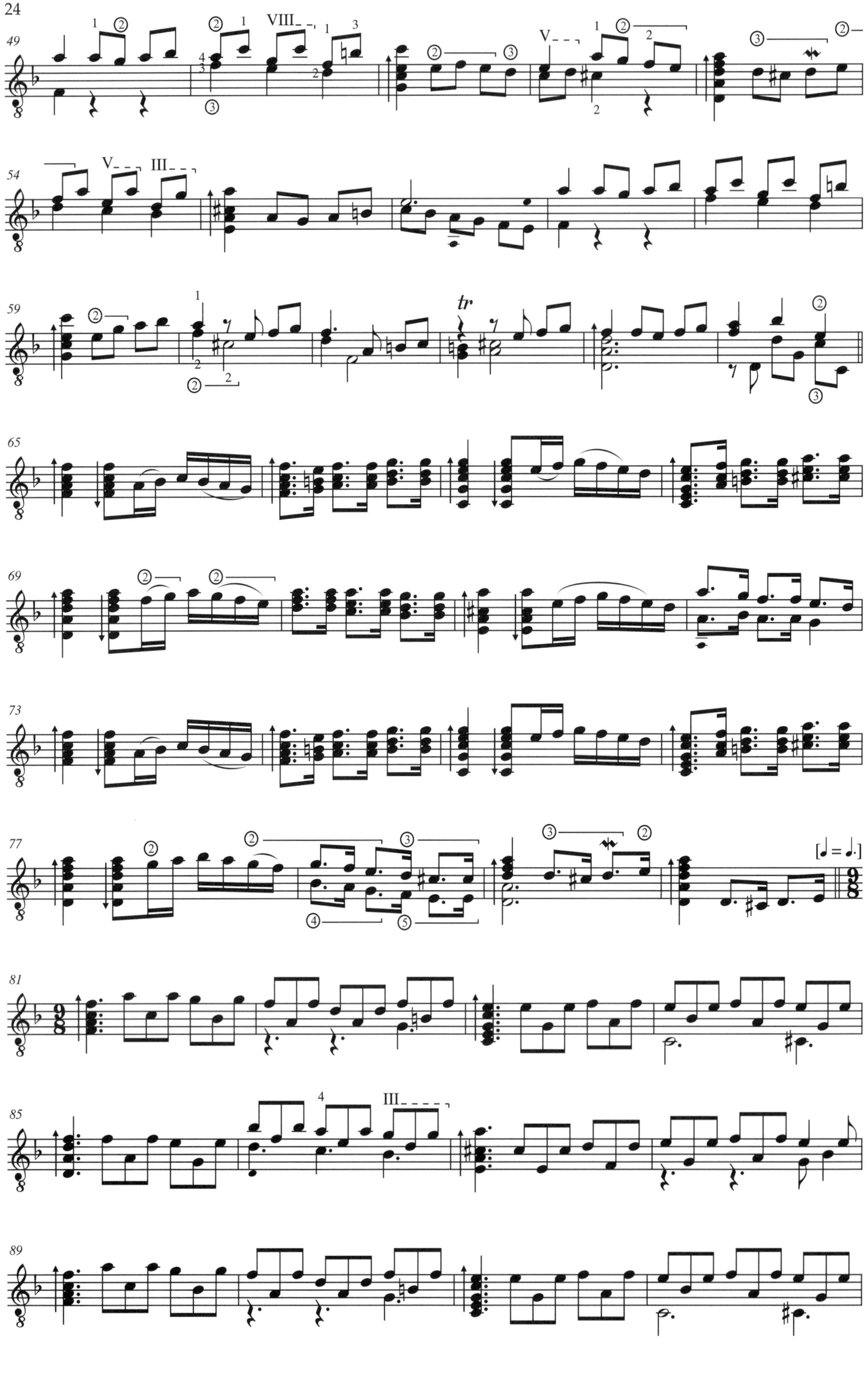
VIII
V
III
tr

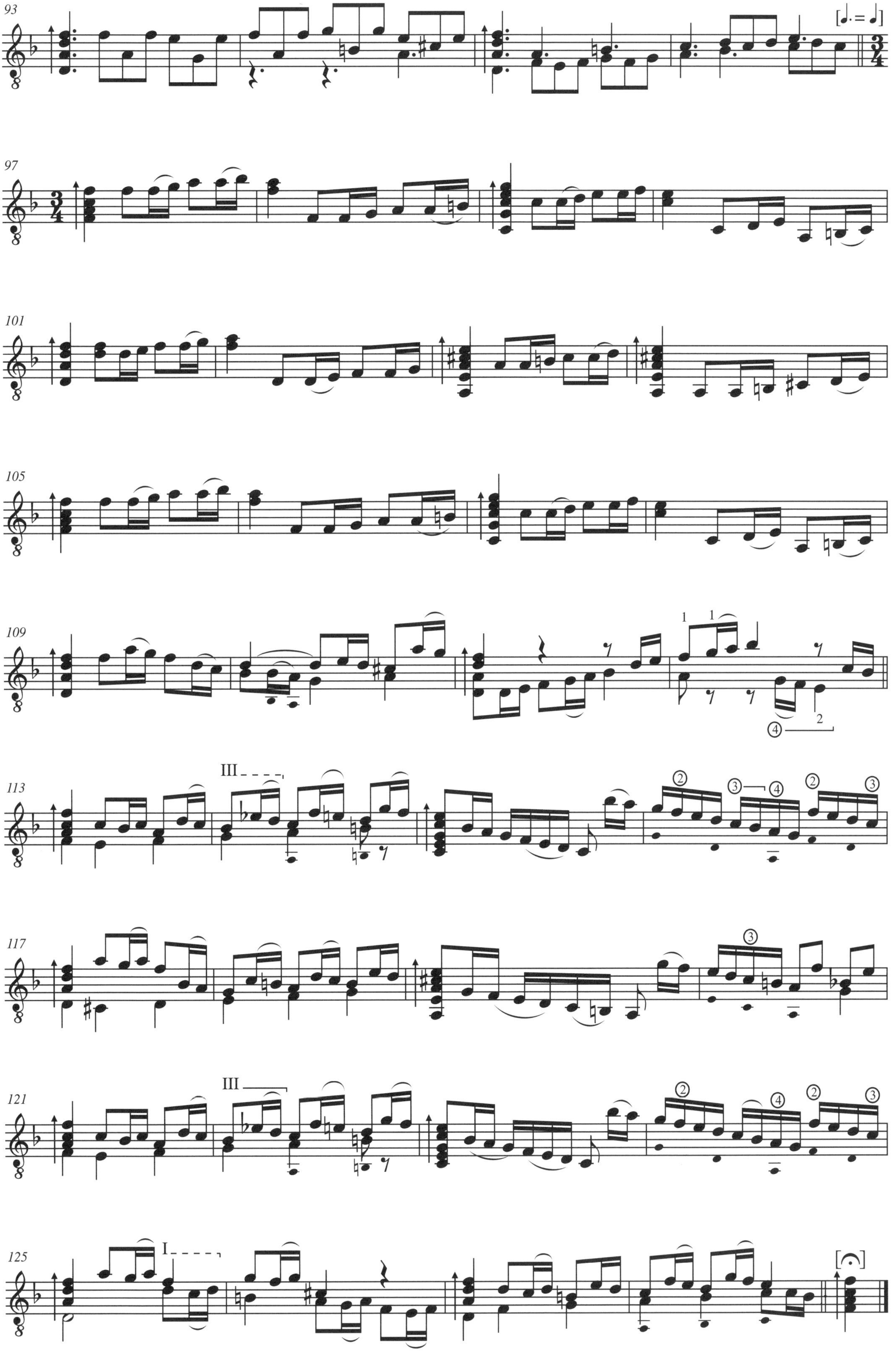
93
[♩. = ♩]
97
101
105
109
113
III
117
121
III
125
I

11. Folías despacio al estilo de Italia

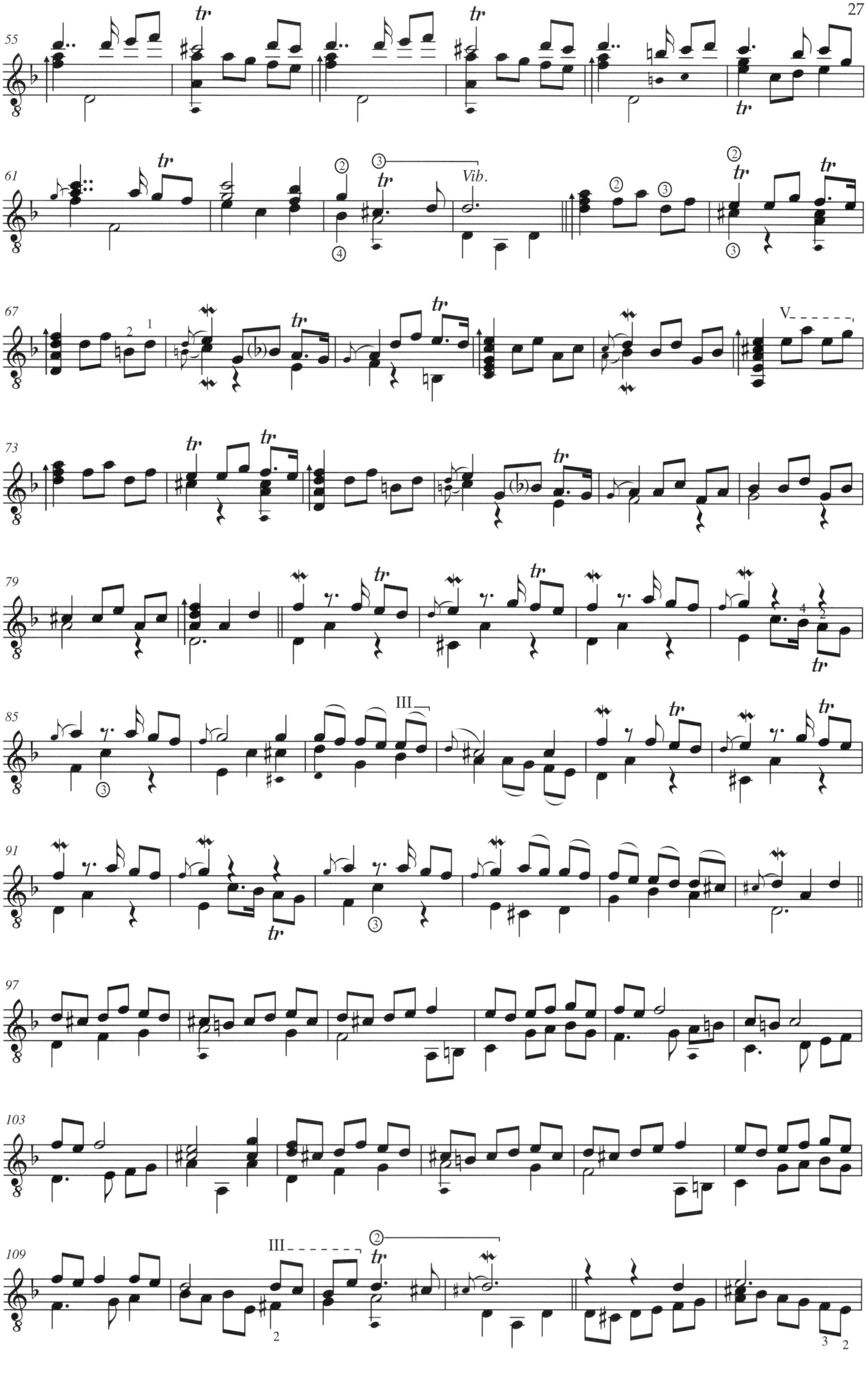
Vib.

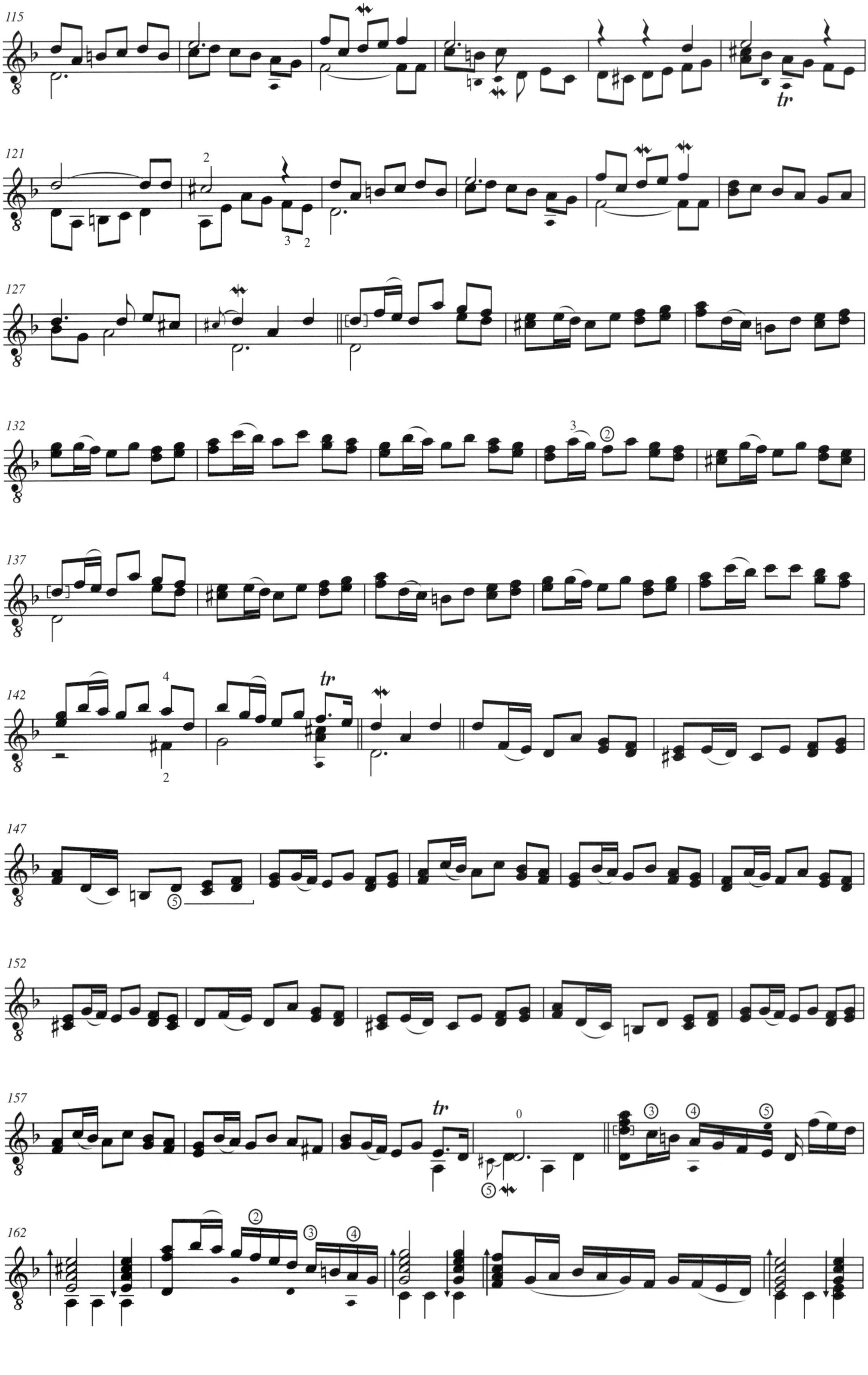
115
121
127
132
137
142
147
152
157
162

29

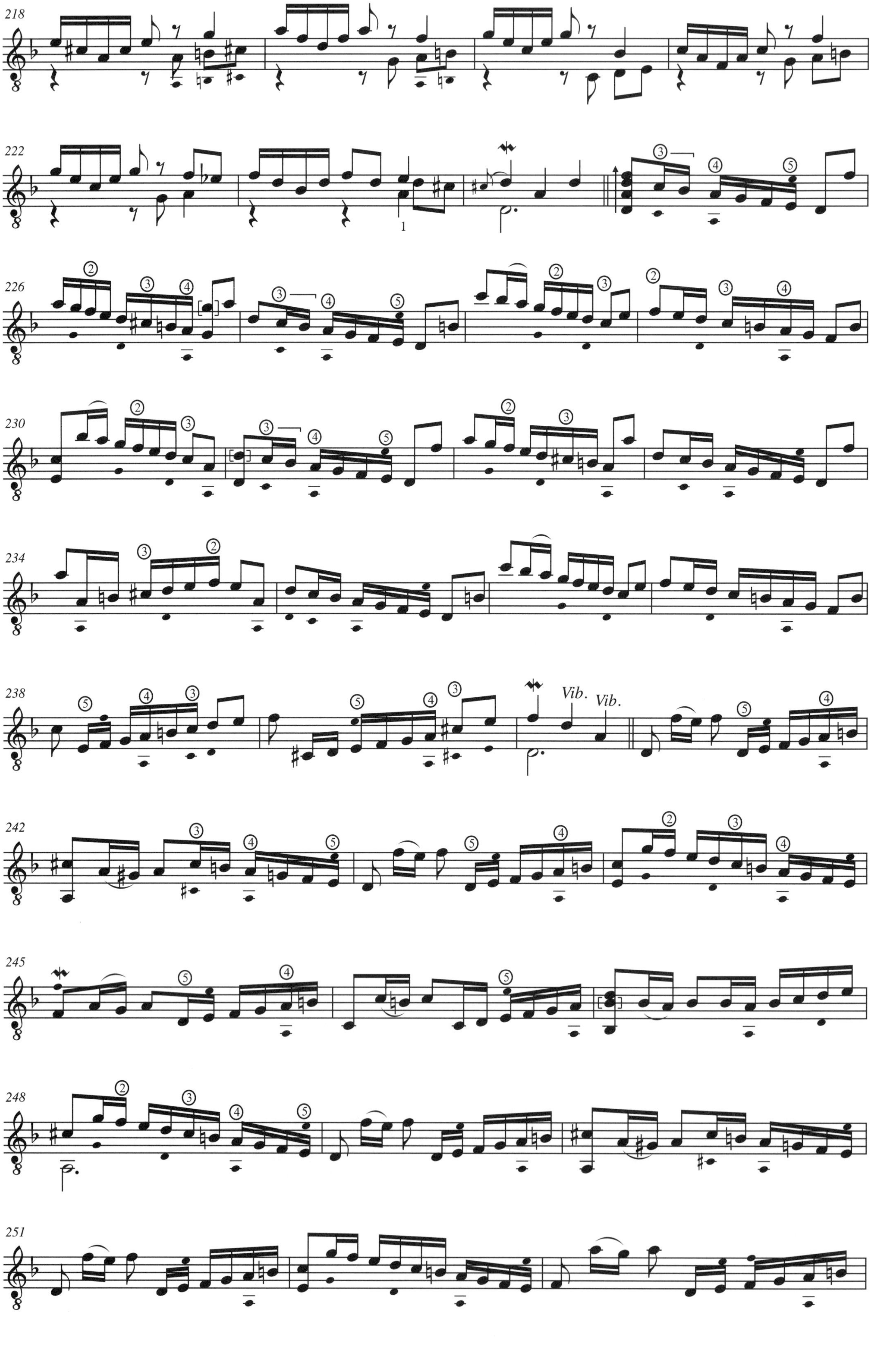
218
222
226
230
234
238
Vib.
Vib.
242
245
248
251

12. Pasacalles de compasillo por la E

13. A proporción por este tono

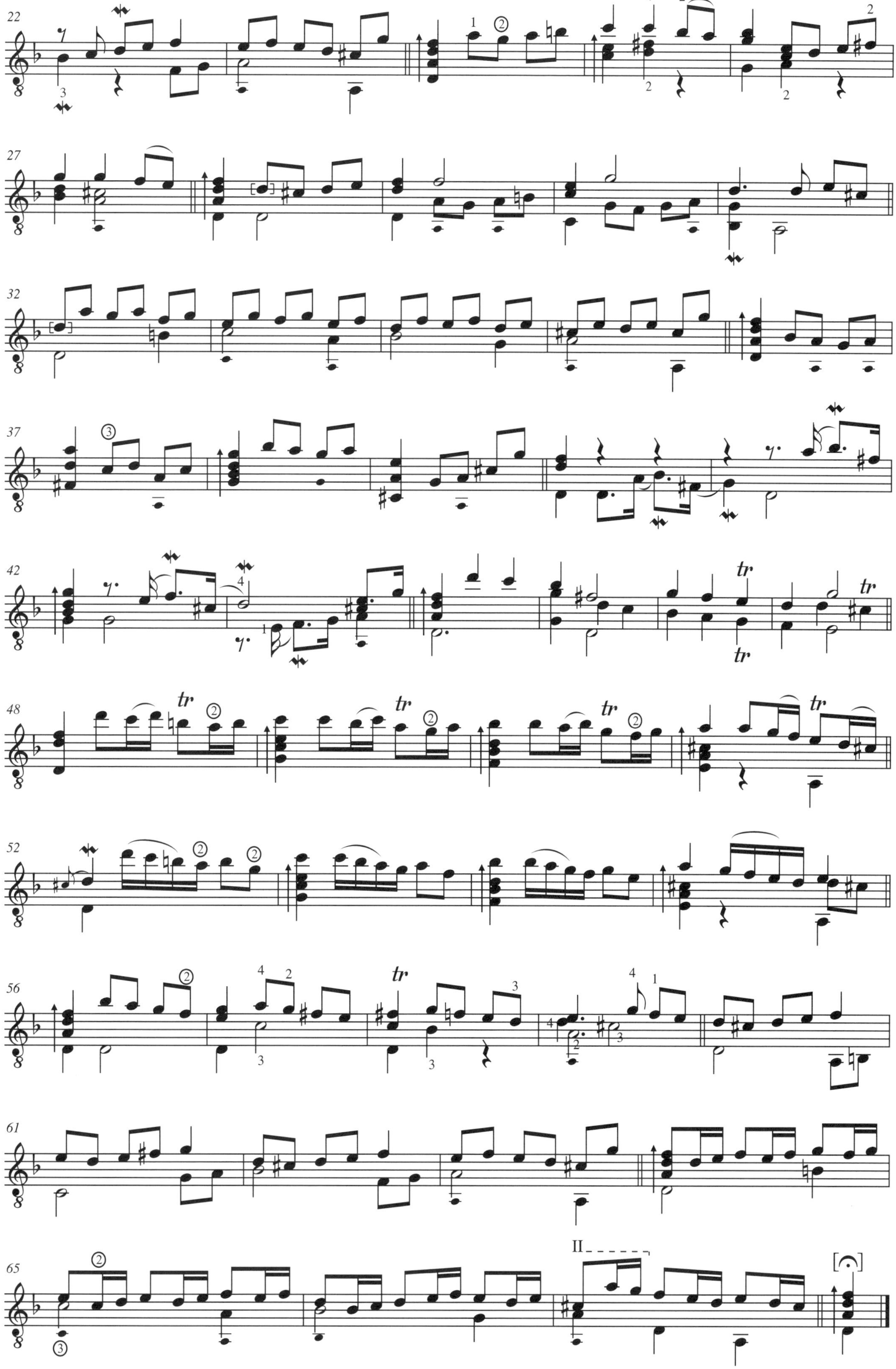
22
27
32
37
42
48
52
56
61
65
tr
II

14. Villanos por la C

Fols. 20v–21r

15. Caballero por la C

Fols. 21r–21v

16. Paradetas por la C

37

17. Canarios por la C

Fols. 23v–24v

18. Menuet fácil

19. Menuet

20. Otro [Menuet]

21. Otro [Menuet]

22. Otro [Menuet]

23. Otro [Menuet]

24. Otro [Menuet]

25. Otro [Menuet]

26. El menuet inglés

27. Menuet

[Fin]

[Al principio]

28. Otro [Menuet]

29. Otro [Menuet]

30. Otro [Menuet]

31. Otro [Menuet] difícil

32. Otro [Menuet]

33. Otro [Menuet]

34. Otro [Menuet]

35. Jácaras de la costa

Fols. 29r–29v

36. El torneo por la C

Fols. 29v–31r

[The second time go to "Últimas reverencias"]

Reverencias

Últimas reverencias

Jácaras del torneo

Gallardas del torneo

37. La Azucena por la E

Fols. 31v–32r

38. Los imposibles por la D

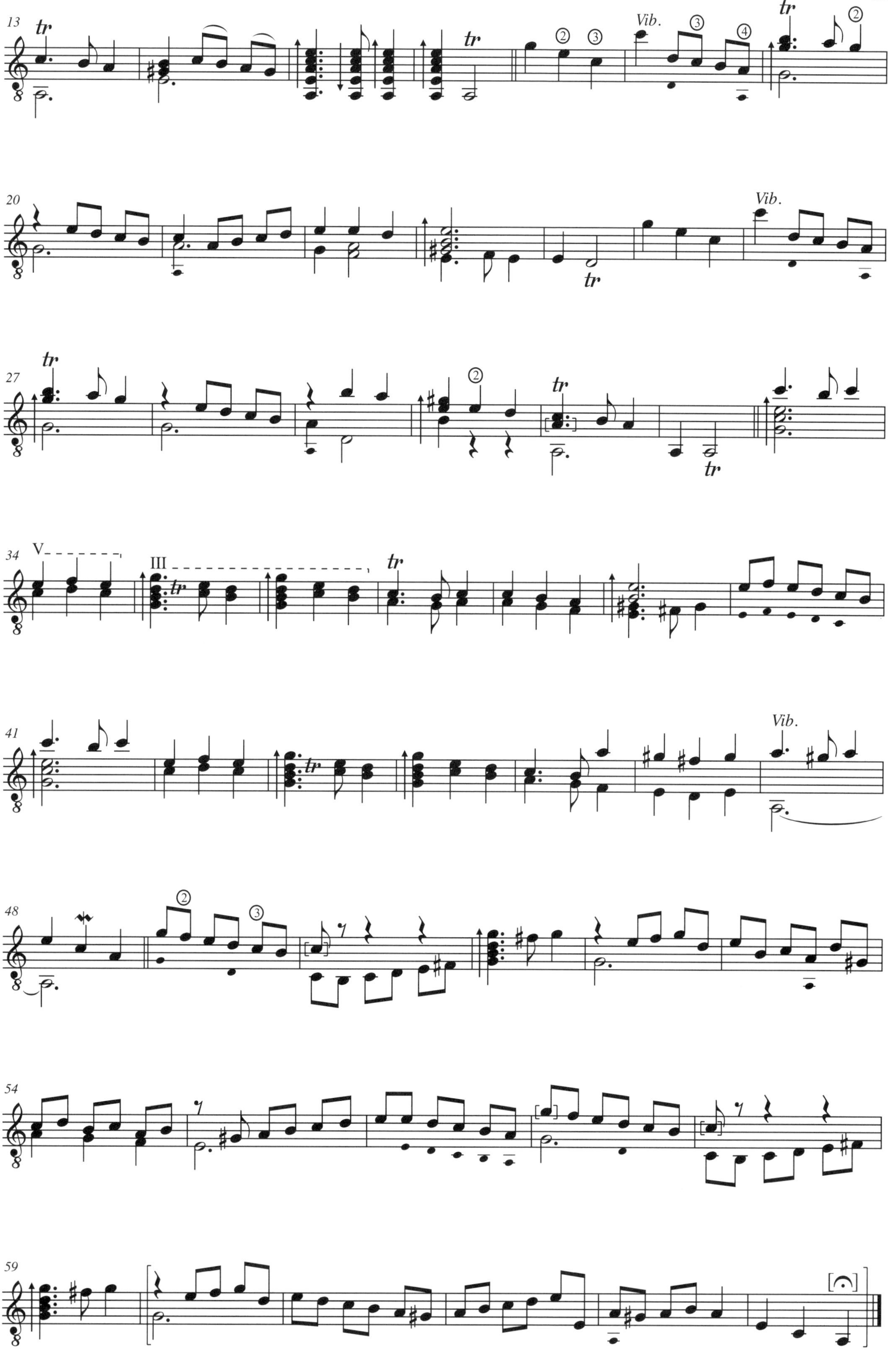
13
tr
Vib.
20
Vib.
27
tr
34
V
III
tr
41
tr
Vib.
48
54
59

39. Cumbé por la A

40. Zarambeques por la C

41. Obra por la C

Alemanda

Fols. 35v–37r

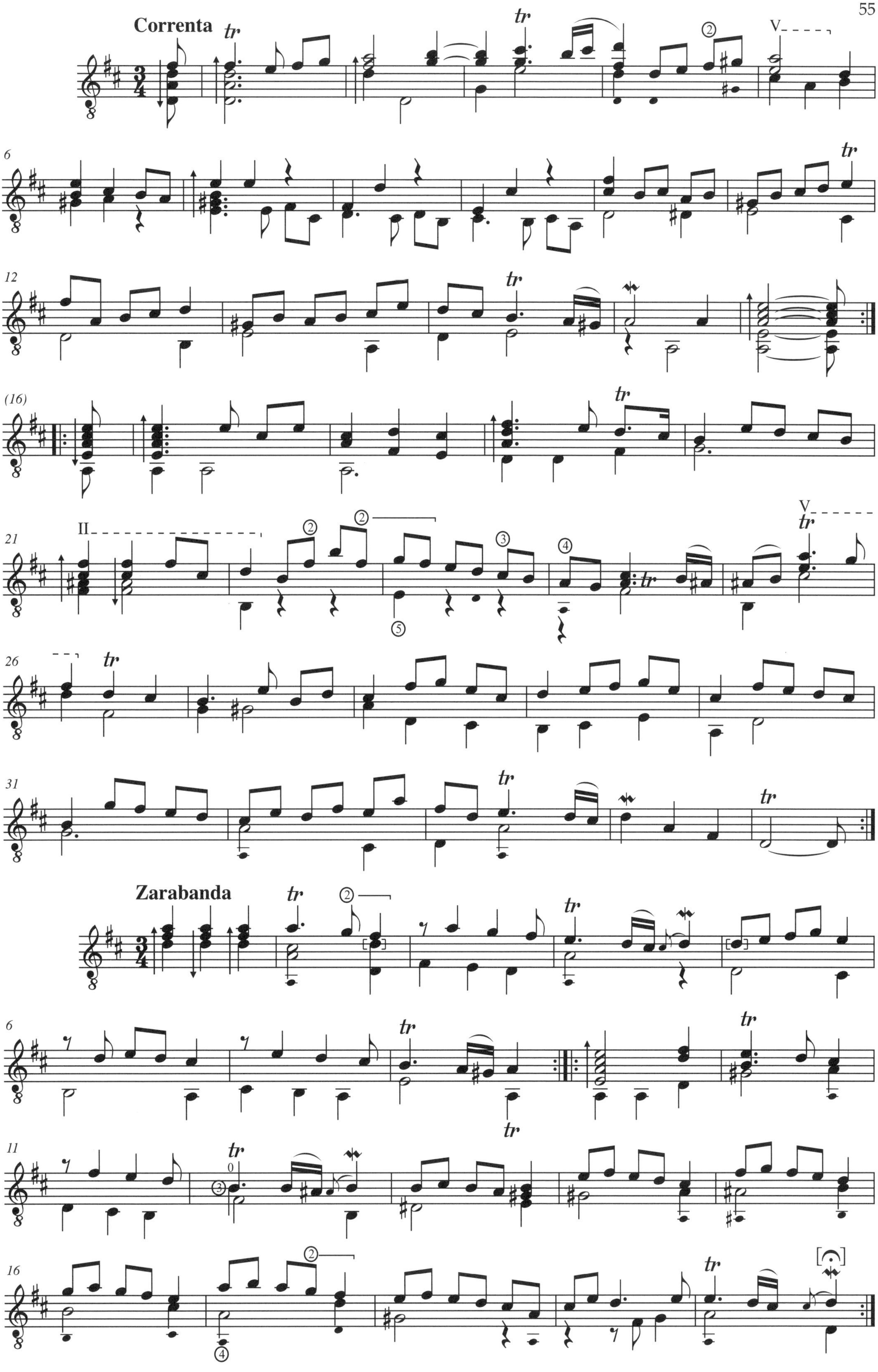
Correnta
Zarabanda

Giga

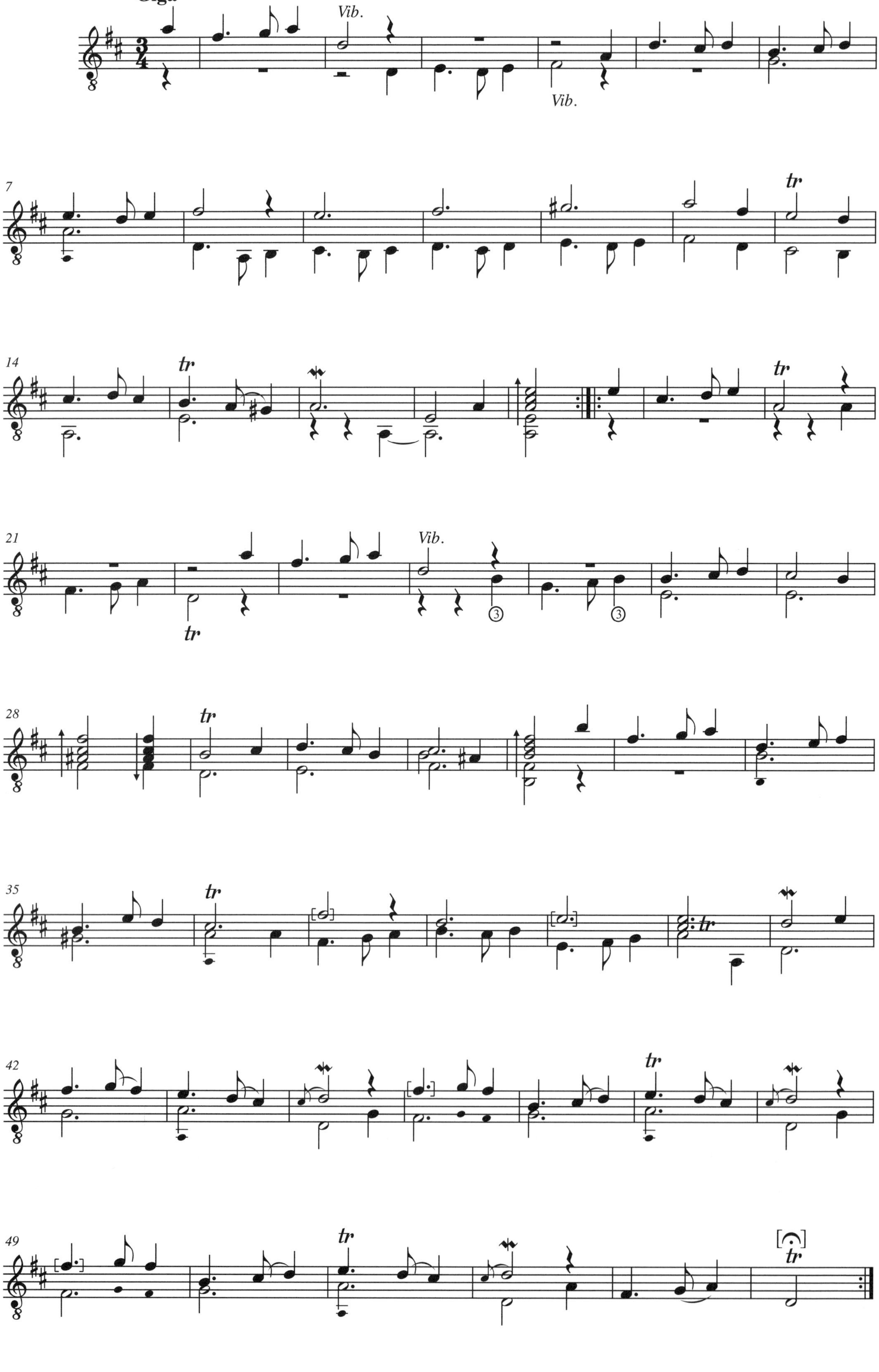

42. Bailad caracoles por la C

Fols. 37v–38r

43. Marsellas por la B

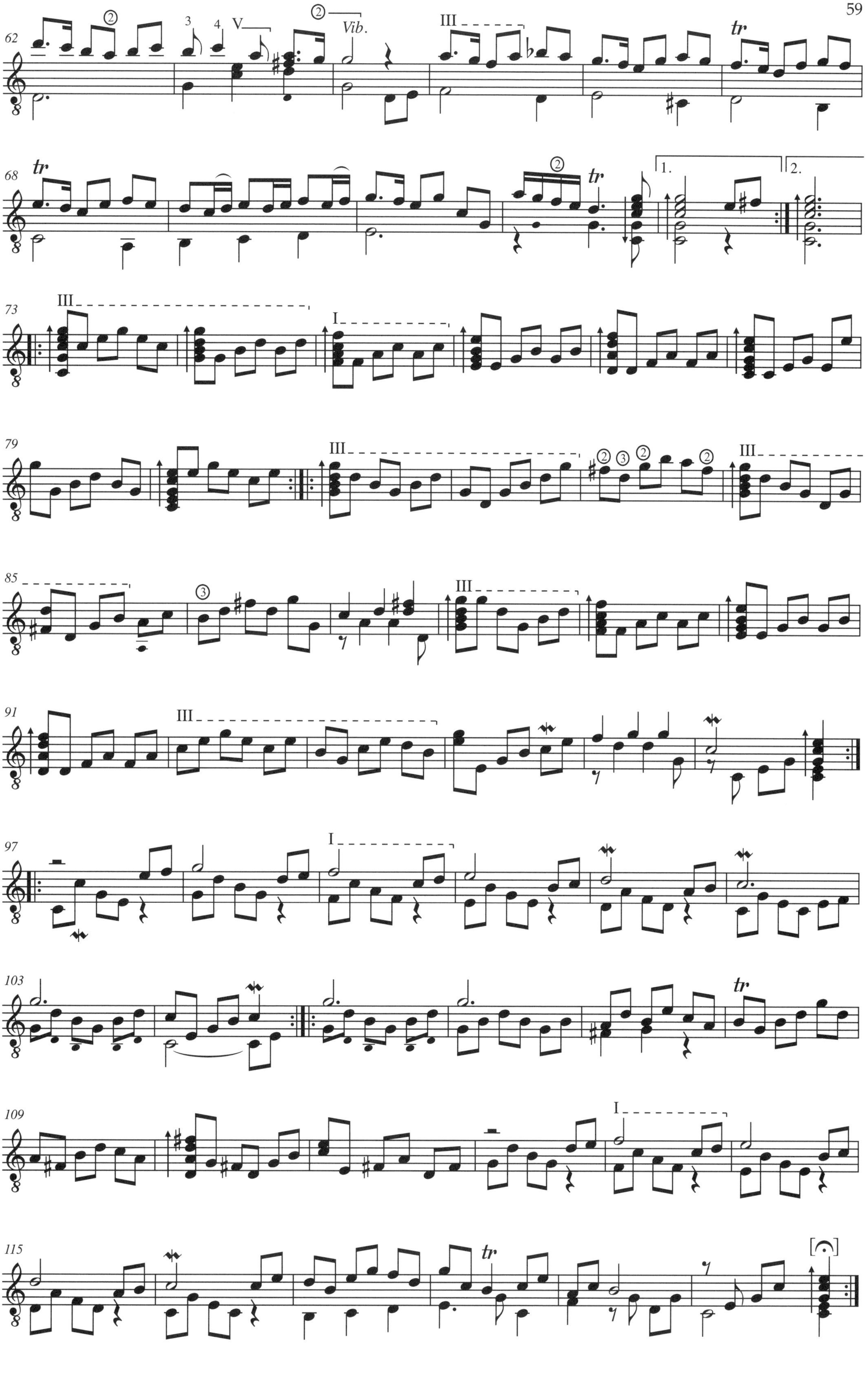
Vib.

44. Canción

45. Marcha de los oboes

46. Marcha valona

47. Marcha de los carabineros

Fols. 40v–41v

48. Marcha de las guardias de la Reina Ana

Fols. 41v–[42r]

49. Paspied nuevo

50. Burée por la D

51. Gavota

52. Gavota

[François Le Cocq / Santiago de Murcia]

53. Idea nueva, y obra especial de clarines

Idea nueva de clarines primorosos por la C

Fols. 45r–50v

Canción airosa

Marcha

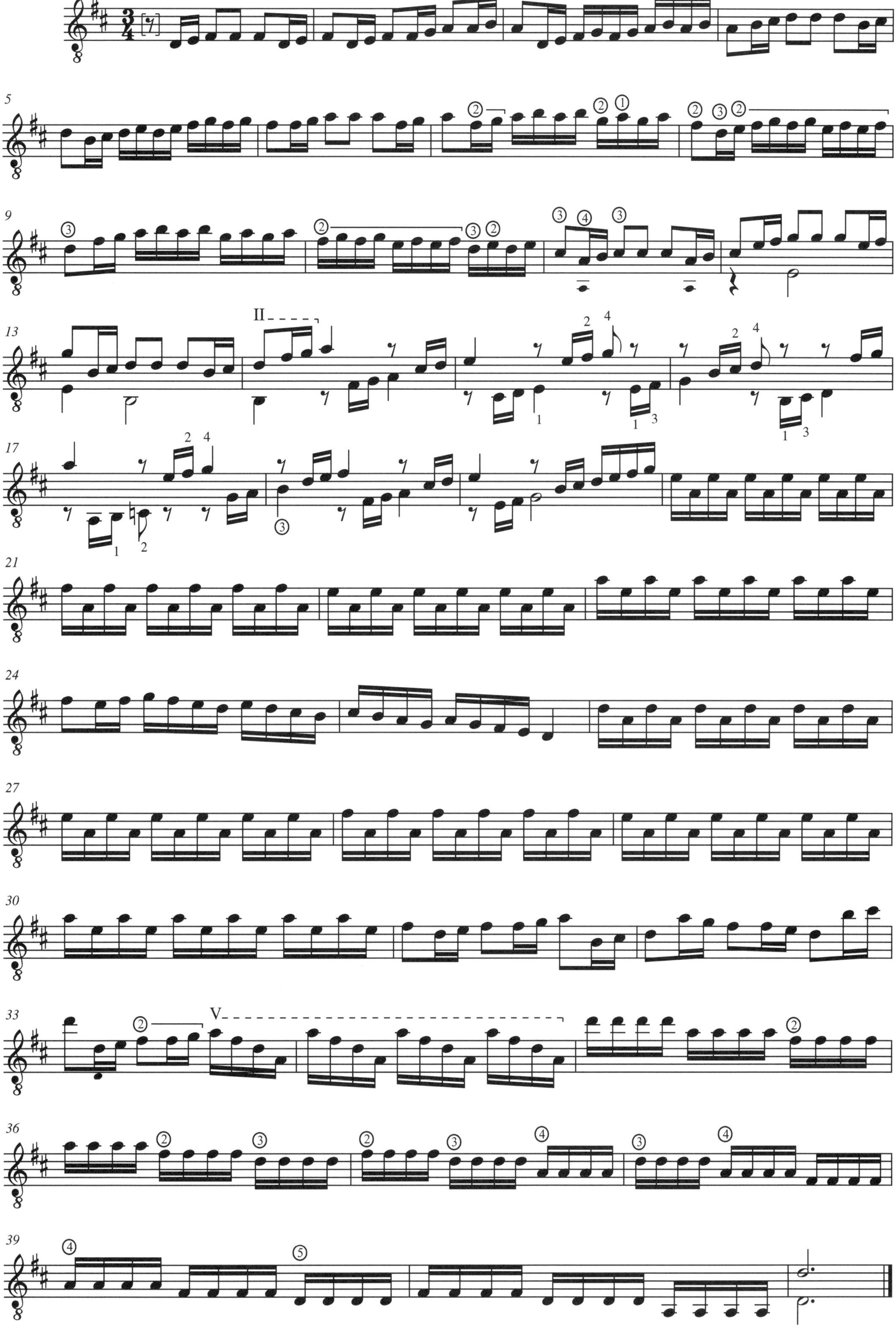

Canción de ecos

Fajina

Idea de dos clarines

69

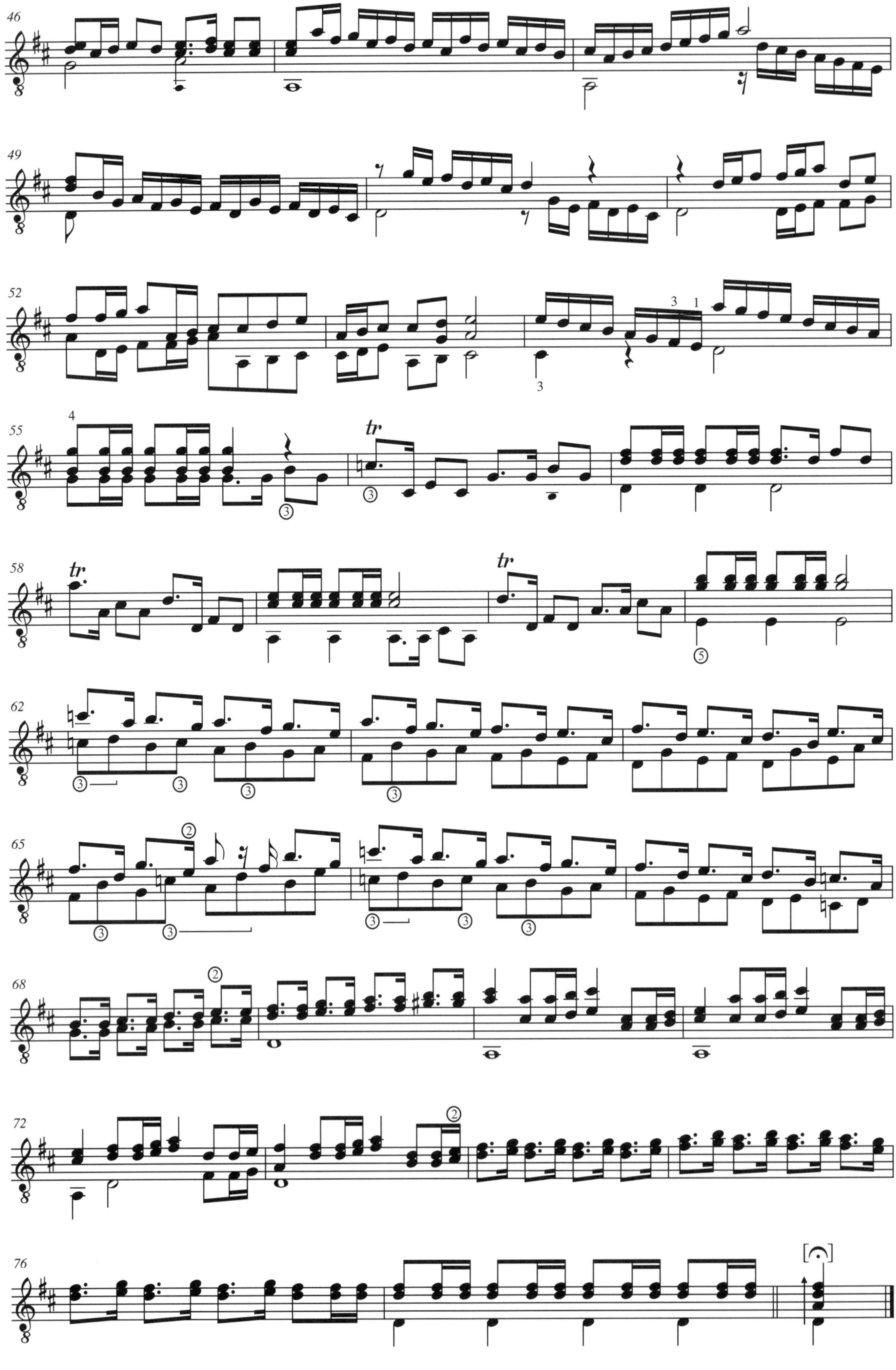
46
49
52
55
tr
58
tr
tr
62
65
68
72
76

54. Obra por la K3

[François Campion]

Preludio por la K3 que es lo mismo que la L

Fols. 50v–52v

Alemanda

Correnta

[Zarabanda]

55. Burée

56. Pasacalles de compasillo por la O

57. A proporción

Fols. 54r–54v

58. Pasacalles de compasillo por el +

Fols. 55r–56v

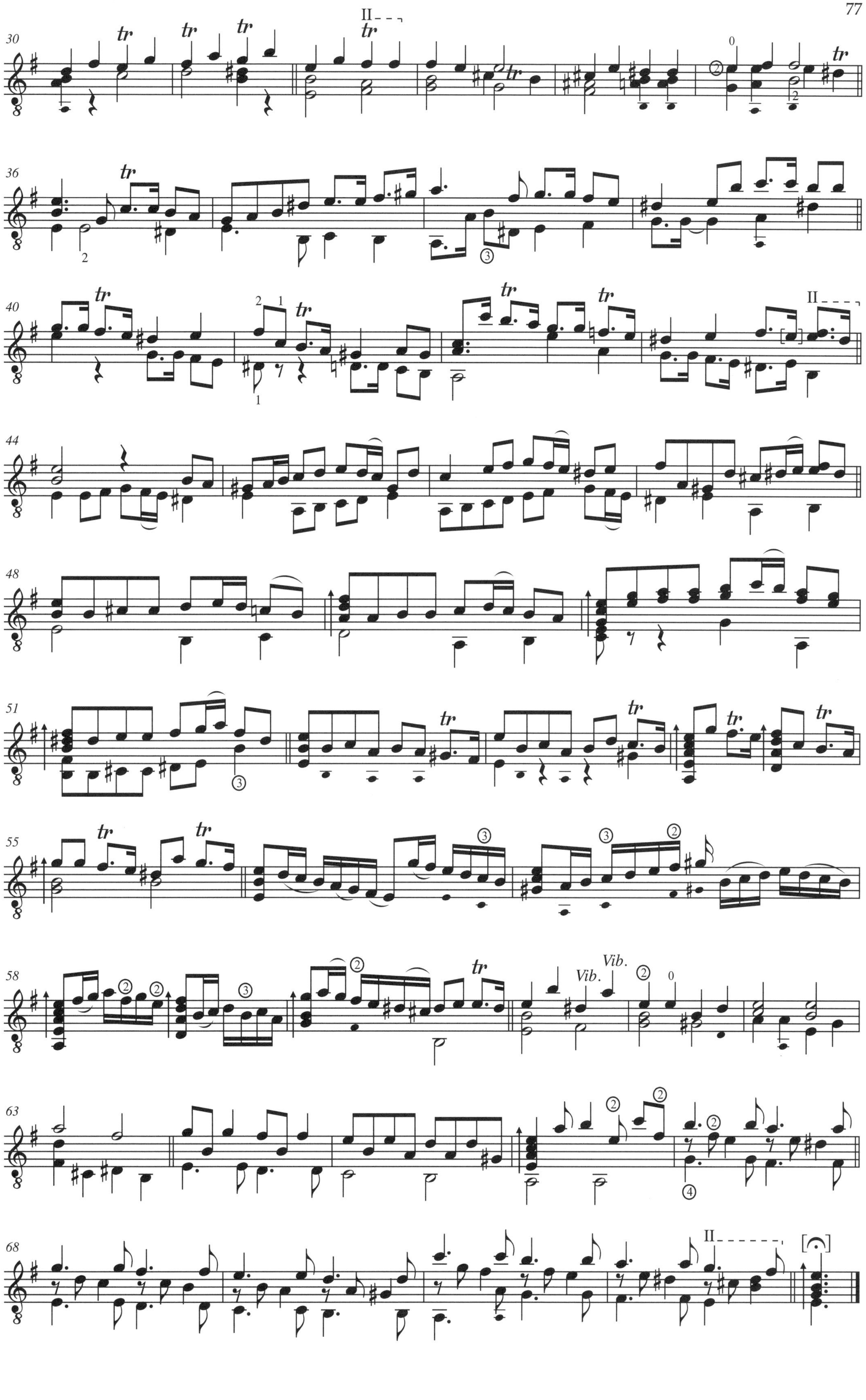
30
II
36
40
44
48
51
55
58
Vib.
Vib.
63
68
II

59. A proporción

60. Pasacalles de compasillo por la B

61. A proporción

62. Pasacalles de compasillo por la G

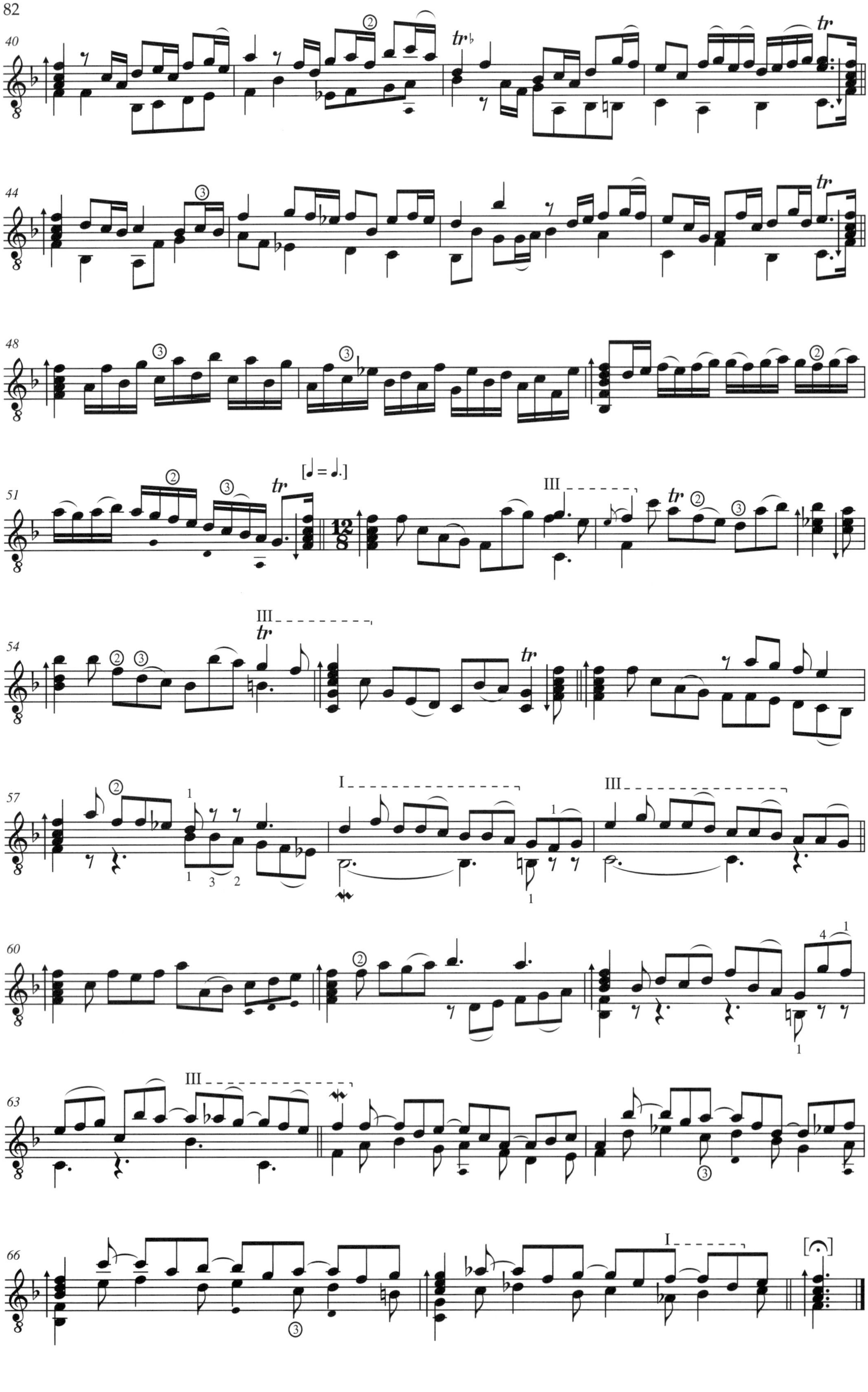

63. A proporción

64. Pasacalles de compasillo por la D

Fols. 62r–63r

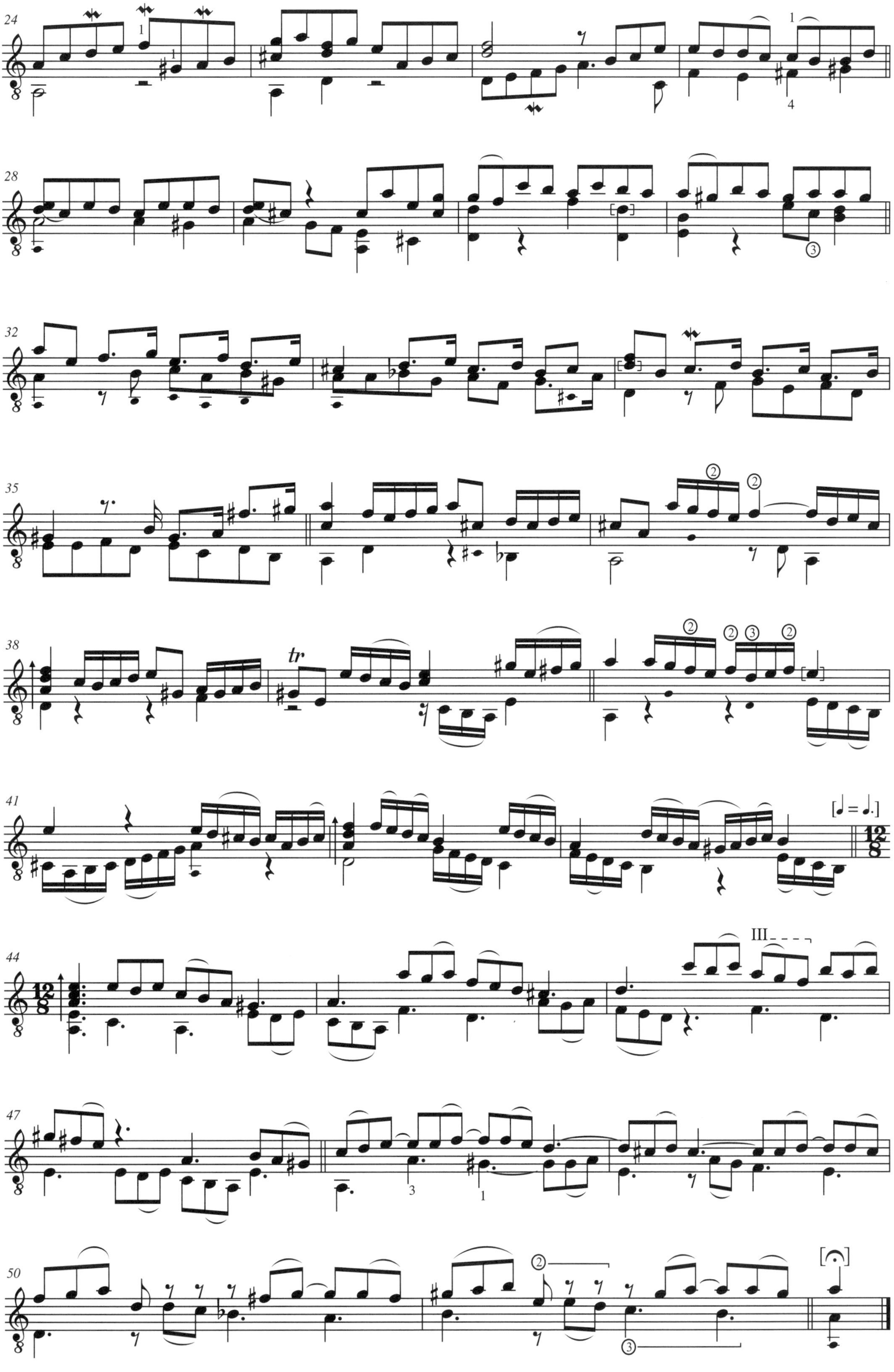
24
28
32
35
38
tr
41
44
III
47
50

65. A proporción

66. Pasacalles aclarinados por la C a compasillo

Fols. 64v–66r

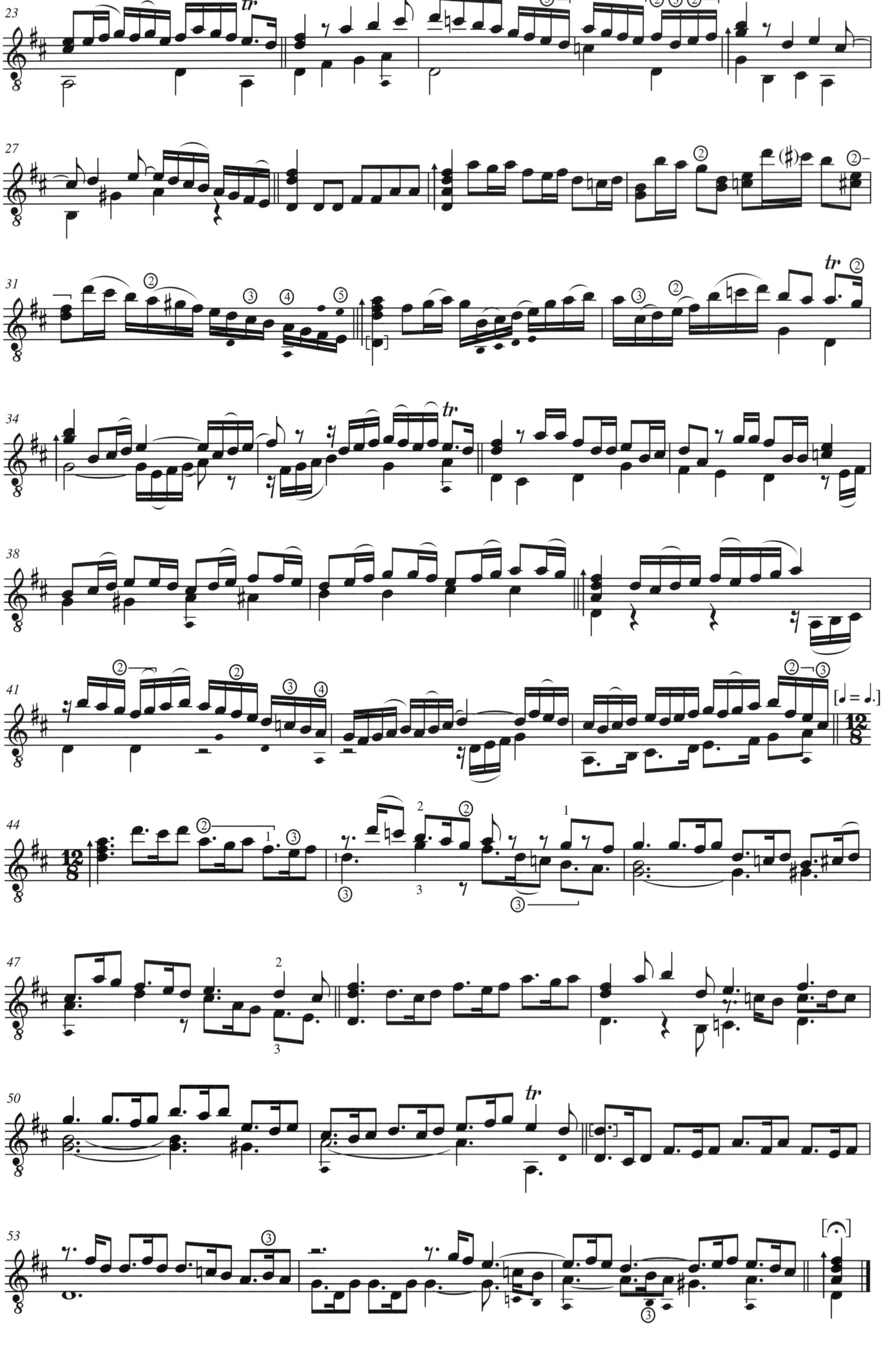

67. Pasacalles a compasillo por la H

Fols. 66r–67v

68. A proporción

Fols. 67v–68v

69. Pasacalles de compasillo por la A

Fols. 68v–69v

70. A proporción

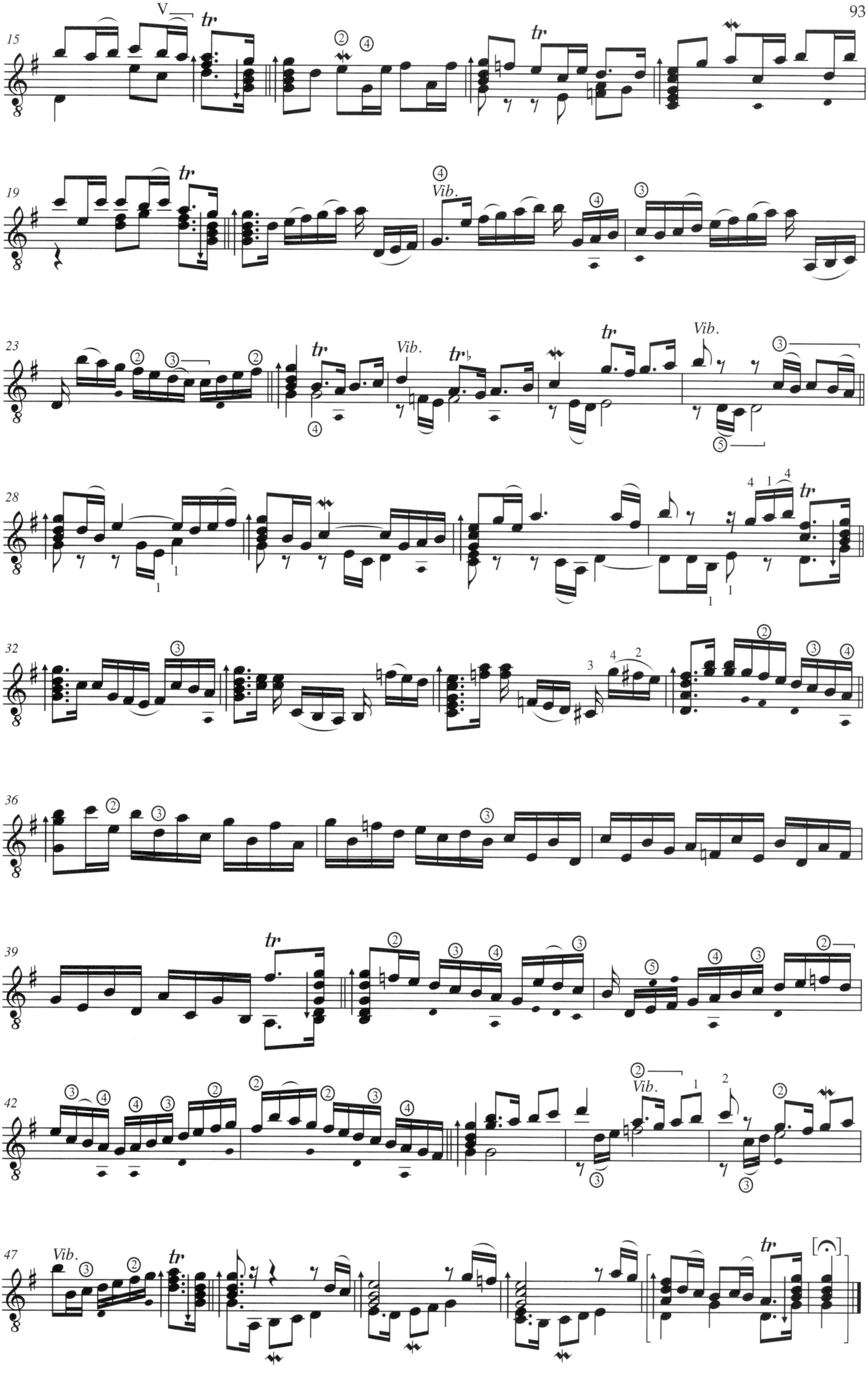
Vib.
Vib.
Vib.
Vib.
Vib.
tr

Critical Report

Editorial Policies

The music gathered in "Cifras selectas de guitarra" was intended for a baroque guitar, that is, an instrument composed of five courses, one single and four double (pairs of strings). While their standardized notes corresponded to the first five strings of the modern guitar, there was a great variety in stringing the fourth and fifth courses: each course could be composed of two upper strings (the so-called re-entrant tuning, d'/d' and a/a), or of an upper and a lower string (bourdon) producing octaves (d/d' and A/a). A few sources even prescribed that the third course could be tuned g/g', and Gaspar Sanz stated that the guitar was occasionally tuned in Spain with two bourdons in the fourth and fifth courses (d/d and A/A), though this system was apparently limited to strummed music. The fact is that several tunings were used in plucked music for that instrument (example 1). On the other hand, the use of upper strings in both the fourth and fifth courses gave rise to some devices in principle alien to the modern guitar, of which the most common was the execution of scales on alternate strings (the so-called *campanelas*), producing a "cascading" or harp-like effect. The upper strings, indeed, reduced—not removed—the octave displacements that such a practice would have produced in a modern instrument. These features support the prevailing opinion among scholars that the best instrument for performing Murcia's music is the baroque guitar.[1]

My transcription should not be interpreted as an attempt to deny that the experience of reading this music directly from the tablature is irreplaceable; the presentation of an unabridged facsimile of the manuscript with this edition has been motivated, precisely, by the wish to facilitate such an experience for contemporary baroque guitarists. Nonetheless, it is a basic tenet of the present edition that a performance on a modern guitar can also represent a legitimate and artistic way of re-creating Murcia's music with an appropriate transcription, that is, one fitting well with the modern instrument but preserving some of the character and idiomatic devices of the baroque guitar. For that reason, the transcriptions presented here do not include any sound below the note A (i.e., the open fifth string of the modern guitar), since, in spite of the many doubts still persisting about the tuning of Murcia's original instrument (discussed below), it is clear that it was unable to surpass such a note in its lower register. This was part of the delicate sound that Murcia refers to in the prologue, a feature that a modern transcription including notes such as G and E would lose. The preservation of the *campanelas* and the use of unstemmed notes, to be discussed below, were adopted with the same purpose. Additionally, I believe that the transcriptions can also be of interest for a baroque guitarist, since they allow for visualizing aspects of the music that the tablature does not explicitly show (especially the voice-leading).[2] In this way, the performer can compare his own interpretation of Murcia's music to that of the present writer.

On the other hand, the transcription has followed the prevailing conventions in the notation of guitar music. The pieces are transcribed with the octave-transposing treble clef, in single staves. The strings are indicated only when necessary by encircled arabic numbers, in accordance with the current practice. Accidentals remain in effect throughout a measure unless cancelled and may be repeated within a measure if more than one voice is involved; cautionary accidentals, in parentheses, are extremely rare and appear only in very doubtful cases (e.g., "Pasacalles aclarinados por la C a compasillo," no. 66, m. 30). The spelling of the titles has been modernized when it has no phonetic value, the abbreviations have been expanded, and numbers 1–70 have been added. The key signatures have been modernized, but the reader is encouraged to consult the discussion about the modal system used by Murcia in the introduction (see "Notation and Theory"). The strummed passages, as well as the direction of the strum, are indicated by an arrow placed to the left of the given chord; the reader must bear in mind that the arrow direction is opposite to that of the stems performing the same function in the original tablature, since it reflects the sequence in which

Example 1. Main tunings for the baroque guitar (source: Tyler and Sparks, *The Guitar and Its Music*, 184–86).

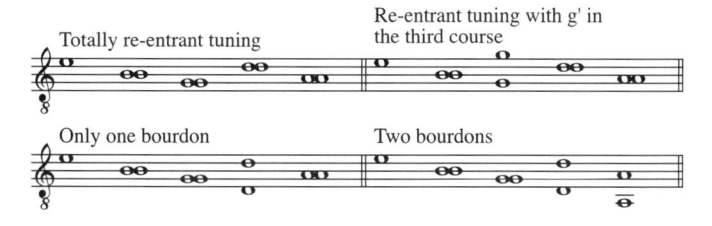

the chord-notes are played and not the physical movement of the hand (i.e., a down-strum is indicated by an ascending arrow, and vice versa).³ With the exception of the left-hand fingering and strings, to be treated later, any note or symbol added by the editor appears in brackets; this is also valid for the sections added in order to complete the pieces that are partly missing (see the critical notes for details). Other aspects deserve a further and independent discussion.

Attributions

As we have seen, a problematic aspect of the manuscript is the inclusion of some borrowed pieces that lack any attribution. Consequently, it is possible that more pieces belong to other composers as well. Nonetheless, both "Cifras selectas" and Murcia's other manuscripts show that the borrowings occur in pieces in foreign style, such as suite movements, minuets, and so on. The *pasacalles* and Spanish dance types were in all likelihood composed by Murcia, which implies that most of the repertory in the manuscript can be provisionally attributed to him. Considering all this, I have preferred to indicate in brackets the name of the composer only when a piece can be attributed *to another composer* with some certitude, namely those by Campion ("Obra por la K3," no. 54) and Le Cocq ("Gavota," no. 52, despite the reservations previously expressed for this under "The Music: An Intertextual Music" in the introduction). The reader can consult table 2 (see the appendix of the introduction) for other possible borrowings (such as in "Idea nueva, y obra especial de clarines," no. 53) and arrangements of pre-existing music (such as "La Azucena por la E," no. 37). Probably future research will provide new attributions for other pieces.

Campanelas

As commented above, the presence on the baroque guitar of upper strings in both the fourth and fifth courses makes it possible to perform scales in alternating courses (*campanelas*). Because the fourth and fifth strings are in the lower register on the modern guitar, most editors have assumed that the *campanelas* were not appropriate to this instrument. Several scalic passages thus appear impoverished and unable to fill the sound space, as though they lack another voice, especially when performed slowly. Nevertheless, the fact is that most of the *campanela* passages can actually be reproduced on the modern guitar with a careful alternation of strings. This demands an additional extension of the left hand, but modern guitarists are certainly used to facing much more difficult problems in the field of technique. As a result, the transcription maintains an important aspect of the music for the baroque guitar (example 2). To my knowledge, the only editor having adopted this procedure is Frank Koonce.⁴ But in the present edition, unlike his, the *campanela* passages are indicated with the strings, assuming that the performer will be able to select an appropriate left-hand fingering (mostly using the index and little fingers). Obviously, the strings have been indicated only for the notes performed in other than the first position

Example 2. Passages with *campanelas*: "Marionas por la B" (fol. 3r [no. 2, mm. 54–55]); "Difrencias de gallardas por la E" (fol. 4r [no. 3, m. 38]); "A proporción" (fol. 64v [no. 65, m. 52]).

(e.g., c′ is indicated when performed in the third string instead of the second). Since the unstemmed notes (discussed below under "Tuning") make those passages easily identifiable, I do not specify them in the critical notes, nor do I discuss other minor changes made in order to adapt a given *campanela* to the modern guitar (occasionally, for instance, it has been necessary to move a note from the first course to the second string).

Dynamic Markings and Written Directives

Dynamic markings and other directives are exceptional in the manuscript and are always written in Spanish. Since I reproduce them literally in the transcription, I offer their translation and meaning as follows:

Al principio: "to the beginning," used on folio 25r at the end of the third minuet (no. 20) to indicate D.C. al Fine; it has been added to the transcription of no. 27 in brackets, leaving to the performer the choice of adding it to other minuets as appropriate.

Eco: dynamic mark equivalent to *piano*;⁵ used on fols. 46r and 48r in "Canción airosa" and "Canción de ecos," respectively, of no. 53.

Fin: "end," used on folio 25r in the middle of the third minuet (no. 20); this also has been added to the transcription of no. 27 in brackets, leaving to the performer the choice of adding it to other minuets as appropriate.

Fuerte: dynamic mark equivalent to *forte*, which seems to denote, in Murcia's usage, a contrast with the *eco* sections instead of a *forte* in the strict sense; it is used on fols. 46r and 48r in "Canción airosa" and "Canción de ecos," respectively, of no. 53.

Otro: "another," indicating a new piece of the same type as the previous one.

Sigue (sing.) or *Siguen* (pl.): literally "follow(s)," indicating that a piece continues on the next page; these directives appear many times in the manuscript but have not been transferred to the transcription.

Left-hand Fingering

As explained in the introduction, Murcia uses dots next to each number to indicate the left-hand fingering, but only until folio 26v (i.e., until the end of the eighth minuet, no. 25), assuming that, at this point, the amateur will have learned to place the appropriate fingers by him or herself. In the transcription I indicate the fingering with arabic numbers in accordance with the modern practice

(1 refers to the index finger, 2 to the middle finger, and so on). Despite the importance of this aspect, I do not specify each finger as Murcia does: such a detailed procedure would have extremely overloaded the staff and, in most cases, the performer can infer the fingering from the musical context. In addition, the pretension of reproducing Murcia's fingering as a whole would have been utopian since the transcription from the five-course guitar to the modern one entails modifications regarding the voicing and voice-leading (see below) that often oblige altering the fingering. Therefore, I have specified the left-hand fingering only in ambiguous passages and where it has implications for the performance.

As regards the pieces lacking these dots (i.e., from "El menuet inglés," no. 26, onwards), editorial fingerings have been occasionally added on the basis of the experience acquired with the previous works, as Murcia recommends. This has been facilitated by his use of standard fingerings for some positions. For example, the fingering of the first chord in measure 15 of "El torneo por la C" (no. 36) is taken from pieces preceding folio 26, in which Murcia always indicates it as such (example 3). The concordant passages in "Passacalles y obras" and "Códice Saldívar" have also been utilized to provide additional fingerings in order to clear up some doubtful passages and facilitate the reading for the guitarist.

The measure from "El torneo por la C" included in example 3 clearly shows the extent to which the left-hand fingering affects the performance, in such a way that the first chord cannot surpass a quarter note. I have adopted an editorial policy of reflecting this aspect in the transcription, since the value of the notes is directly related to articulation and phrasing (see the introduction under "Notes on Performance"). Nonetheless, in spite of the accuracy of the copy, some concordant passages with "Códice Saldívar" and "Passacalles y obras" prove that Murcia's fingering is not exempt from slips. Consequently, I have occasionally modified it in order to facilitate presumed musical intentions in the sphere of voice-leading. These changes are specified in the critical notes.

Lines and Repeats

The oblique lines used by Murcia to indicate sustaining some notes have been omitted. He does not utilize such lines in a consistent way and they can be deduced in most cases from either the rhythmic values or the position of the left hand. For example, in measure 25 of "Tarantelas por la E" (no. 9) where Murcia indicates such lines, no performer would attempt to separate the eighth notes within each beat.

The line or bar below the staff in the facsimile, indicating a *barré* chord or passage, has been notated with a horizontal bracket above the staff in the transcriptions, according to the prevailing practice. I have added a roman numeral in order to specify the fret to be *barré*, leaving to the performer the choice of the number of strings to be spanned by the index finger.[6] It is evident that Murcia indicates many fewer bars than he actually used. The fingering proves that even some positions that could have easily been executed with different fingers are

Example 3. A standard fingering for the left hand: "Folías despacio al estilo de Italia" (fol. 15v [no. 11, m. 142]); "A proporción por este tono" (fol. 19v [no. 13, m. 9]); "Villanos por la C" (fol. 20v [no. 14, m. 14]); "Caballero por la C" (fol. 21r [no. 15, m. 7]); "Canarios por la C" (fol. 23v [no. 17, m. 19]); "El torneo por la C" (fol. 29v [no. 36, m. 15]).

actually *barré* (e.g., "Españoletas por la E," no. 5, m. 9). For that reason, the transcriptions occasionally include bars added by the editor on the basis of the fingering or strings (with dashed lines), and others taken from concordant passages in "Passacalles y obras" and "Códice Saldívar" (specified in the critical notes). The bars implied by some chords of the *alfabeto* can be easily inferred by the performer and have been omitted in order not to overload the score, while a few bars impossible to properly execute on the modern guitar (e.g., "Difrencias de gallardas por la E," fol. 4r, last staff [no. 3]) have been removed without further indications.

The stylized barlines used by Murcia to demarcate variations (see the introduction under "The Music: Notation and Theory") have been transcribed as double-thin barlines. Regarding the half double barlines appearing in the manuscript, I have adopted two different criteria, reproducing them as such when used in the *diferencias,* but replacing them by a double-thin barline when used in binary dances (minuets, gavottes, etc.). The dots indicating a repeat have been kept but modernized, putting them at the end of the first section, and both at the beginning and end of the second section in binary dances and other pieces. Exceptionally, the repeat of a given section demands two different endings, but only the rhythmic value for the second ending is notated by Murcia (e.g., "Marsellas por la B," fol. 38r [no. 43]). In these cases I use two distinct measures spanned with numbered brackets to differentiate between the first and second ending, in keeping with the prevailing practice (the additional measure is not included in the measure numbering of the transcriptions).

Ornaments

I modernize the notation of the ornaments as appropriate (trill, mordent). The performer should remember that, according to Murcia, the execution of the trill must begin on the upper auxiliary note (see "Notes on Performance"). When such a note seems doubtful to me, I specify it with an accidental to the right of the main symbol, occasionally applying the same procedure to the mordent. All the same, the fact that these ornaments are always entrusted to the left hand (never executed in double courses or strings) contributes to clearing up most doubts. Converging slurs (e.g., "Pavanas por la E," fol. 5v, penultimate measure [no. 4, m. 65]) have been combined into a single one, given that their only function in the manuscript is to differentiate between ascending and descending scales (see "Notation and Theory"). The appoggiatura is notated with a small eighth note slurred to the main note; the actual value of the former—roughly a half of the main note—is left to the performer. Vibrato is indicated with the abbreviation "Vib." in italics. Murcia indicates vibrato for each note of a chord, but, in order to simplify the notation, I prefer to indicate it only once above the entire chord (e.g., "Marionas por la B," no. 2, m. 2). All the ornaments are placed over the staff when they affect the upper voice, below it when they affect the bass, and to the right of the note when they affect an inner voice.

Rhythm and Meter

I have attempted not to indicate rhythmic values that are impossible to be performed on the guitar, considering the left-hand fingering and strings. Partly following Maurice Esses,[7] I also do not sustain a note when another is consecutively played on the same string. A few exceptions occur when the two notes are identical, since in such cases the first note can be maintained despite the brief interruption produced by the appearance of the second (e.g., "El Amor por la E," no. 8, m. 26). Unless the contrary is indicated in the critical notes, the transcription keeps the original rhythmic values, although developing the different parts involved in the composition according to the voice-leading. The last note of the *diferencias*, which commonly do not fill the entire measure, is also transcribed with its original value, but a fermata in brackets has been added over it.

Regarding time signatures, the *proporción* sign (3 or Z) has been transcribed as $\frac{3}{4}$ in keeping with the rhythmic values of the pieces. For the same reason, I have used the signature $\frac{3}{8}$ for "Zarambeques por la C" (no. 40) and $\frac{3}{2}$ for the "Correnta" of "Obra por la K3" (no. 54). The time signature $\frac{3}{4}$, appearing in two minuets, has been maintained. The *compasillo* has been transcribed as such with the time signature **C**, although the reader should consider the difference between the modern "common time" and the two types of *compasillo* in the early eighteenth century. I also keep the time signature ₵ in the four pieces where it appears, but the sign 2 at the beginning of "Marcha de las guardias de la Reina Ana" (fol. 41v [no. 48]) has been transcribed as $\frac{2}{2}$. The difference is important since 2 apparently indicated a faster tempo than ₵ (see "Notation and Theory"). The proportional signs $\frac{12}{8}$ and $\frac{6}{8}$ are transcribed as such given their correspondence to the modern notation, but the *sexquinona* $\frac{6}{9}$ in "Las vacas por la C" (fol. 12r [no. 10]) is transcribed as a compound triple meter, $\frac{9}{8}$. The time signature $\frac{6}{4}$ indicated in "Canarios por la C" (fol. 23v [no. 17]) has been replaced by $\frac{6}{8}$ in keeping with the rhythmic values. Since in the modern system these symbols have lost their proportional meaning, I use the equation ♩ = ♩. in brackets to indicate the tempo equivalence when the metrical change occurs within a single piece.

Texture

I generally transcribe the music in a two-voice texture, since it is most commonly used in the manuscript. Notwithstanding, some idiomatic passages with scales and arpeggios have been transcribed in a free, non-contrapuntal way. I use a three-voice texture in more contrapuntal passages, which are rare (e.g., "Pasacalles de compasillo por el +," no. 58, mm. 67–71). Murcia never uses a fourth voice in a strict sense.

Instrumental music, especially with plucked instruments, often allows a free treatment of voices. Even in contrapuntal passages a lower voice can be transformed into an upper one as a result of a large scale, or a given voice can appear or disappear without prior warning (despite the temporal distance, the lute music by Francesco da Milano represents an outstanding example).[8] Both for this reason and in order to simplify the notation, I have adopted the following policies: (1) The appearance of an inner voice in the upbeat is not always preceded by rests (e.g., "Pavanas por la E," no. 4, m. 9), and, likewise, its interruption before ending a measure is not always followed by rests to fill such a measure; occasionally, this criterion has also been applied to the bass (e.g., "Jácaras por la E," no. 1, m. 64). (2) The rhythmic values for the notes performing an accompanimental or harmonic function are frequently fitted to a melodic voice, leaving to the performer the choice of sustaining them when possible. For instance, in "Españoletas por la E," no. 5, measure 17, the e' in the first string has been fitted to the c#' in the second string because the latter is part of the main melody. However, it is possible and even recommendable to perform the former as a dotted half note. (3) Some passages that were probably intended to represent two different voices have been transcribed in a single part, avoiding the appearance of somewhat superfluous rests (e.g., "Idea de dos clarines," mm. 34–36, in "Idea nueva, y obra especial de clarines," no. 53). In short, my purpose has been to simplify the transcription whenever possible while respecting those passages intended as homophonic (melody and accompaniment) or contrapuntal.

Tuning

Undoubtedly, one of the most puzzling and controversial aspects is establishing the appropriate tuning of Murcia's instrument, since he does not say anything about this in either his previous sources or in "Cifras selectas de guitarra." Neil Pennington states that the likelihood is Murcia used a totally re-entrant tuning (the first type in example 1) because of the frequent *campanelas*, but he transcribes the fourth and fifth courses in the lower octave to facilitate the execution on both a baroque and modern guitar.[9] Monica Hall affirms that a bourdon only in the fourth course (third type) ensures the best musical results, an opinion also shared by Craig Russell, who adds some evidence taken from a plucked cadence.[10] Richard Savino considers the tuning with bourdons in the fourth and fifth courses (fourth type) as the most likely.[11] And Michael Lorimer suggests a particular tuning (close to the second type) consisting of a bourdon in the fourth course and an upper octave string (g′) in the third.[12]

The problem is all the more complex since it is possible that Murcia owned several guitars and so used different tunings for different pieces.[13] For instance, the "Pasacalles a compasillo por la H" (no. 67) seems to have been composed for a guitar with bourdons both in the fourth and fifth courses; "Cumbé por la A" (no. 39) can be easily performed with a totally re-entrant tuning; and the *pasacalles* por la E "A proporción por este tono" (no. 13) sound extremely well with a bourdon only in the fourth course.

A preliminary analysis of the music itself seems to strengthen this theory. For instance (see example 4), measure 51 of "Españoletas por la E" (no. 5) implies a bourdon only in the fourth course, in order to preserve the same motive of the previous measure; a cadence of "Villanos por la C" (no. 14) suggests bourdons both in the fourth and fifth courses; measure 9 of "El Amor por la E" (no. 8) supposes an upper string in the third course, otherwise the octave displacement seems unacceptable, even on a baroque guitar; measure 21 of "Pasacalles de compasillo por la D" (no. 64) also supports the same tuning, since the g′, indicated in the first course, appears in the third course in the version of "Passacalles y obras" (fol. 20v); and measures 10–11 of "Jácaras de la costa" (no. 35) suggest a totally re-entrant tuning. Nevertheless, the puzzle has not been totally resolved, as it is very common that *a single piece points to different tunings*. For example, in "Marcha de los carabineros" (no. 47) two consecutives measures treat the fifth course in the lower and upper register; and the same thing occurs in the abovementioned "Pasacalles de compasillo por la H" (no. 67) (example 5). This ambiguity is, perhaps, the most distinctive feature of the baroque guitar, in which all pitches often "melt into one octaveless class."[14] But it could be because, in practice, when the bourdon is placed below the upper string, it is possible to pluck only the latter with the thumb, or at least to partly hide the bourdon's sound. Therefore, although the performance of the *campanelas* is undoubtedly easier with a totally re-entrant tuning, Murcia could perform them even if he used one or two bourdons.[15] In other words, the doubleness of the fourth, fifth, and third courses seem to have been what caused the different registers in the baroque guitar to be less clearly distinguishable. In that case, it seems likely that Murcia used a guitar with two bourdons, as suggested by Savino. But, whatever was its actual tuning, the fact is that the three lower courses are treated in his music in two different registers.

The point thus is how to transcribe such music for an instrument in which the doubleness disappears, since it only has single strings. In my opinion, the best solution is to transcribe the third, fourth, and fifth courses in the upper, lower, or both octaves depending on the musical context.[16] In the latter case, the note added by the editor is indicated in brackets. Nonetheless, the ambiguity of the baroque guitar does not stop there. Example 6 shows two cases in which the first course is inserted in scales *as though it were in the lower octave*. That is, the octaveless context of the instrument allows Murcia to treat ambigu-

Example 4. Passages supporting different tunings: "Españoletas por la E" (fol. 7r [no. 5, mm. 50–51]); "Villanos por la C" (fol. 21r [no. 14, m. 36]); "El Amor por la E" (fol. 9v [no. 8, m. 9]); "Pasacalles de compasillo por la D" (fol. 62v [no. 64, m. 21]); same passage in "Passacalles y obras" (fol. 20v); "Jácaras de la costa" (fol. 29r [no. 35, mm. 10–11]).

Example 5. Contradictory information about tunings: "Marcha de los carabineros" (fol. 41r [no. 47, mm. 33–34]) and "Pasacalles a compasillo por la H" (fol. 66v [no. 67, mm. 19–20]).

ously even those courses clearly tuned in only one register. Since there is no reason in these examples to transpose the entire scales to the upper register, the most simple and convincing solution consists of transcribing the first course as a lower one. Even more controversial, though exceptional, is my transcription of measure 68 of "Españoletas por la E" (no. 5), in which I had to interpret the open fifth course as a treble a′; nonetheless, the c″ following it supports this solution (example 7). Obviously, my purpose has not been to remove all the octave displacements—it is as impossible as it is unnecessary—but to supply a transcription that better reflects the nature of such passages, evidently thought of as linear scales instead of broken melodies. And this purpose has supposed decisions of a critical and interpretive nature at any moment.[17]

Finally, I have used unstemmed noteheads of a smaller size to indicate where a given course has been interpreted

Example 6. First course transcribed in the lower octave: "Pavanas por la E" (fol. 4v [no. 4, mm. 5–6]) and "Folías despacio al estilo de Italia (fol. 17r [no. 11, m. 225]).

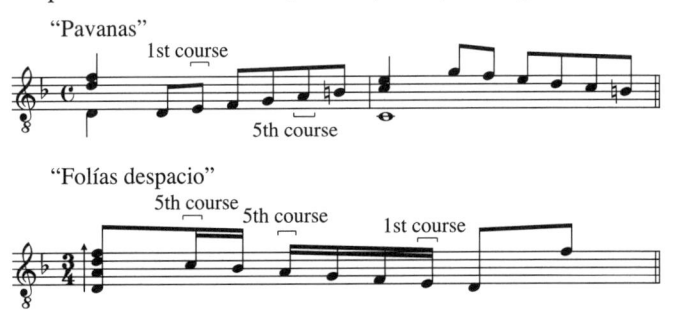

Example 7. Exceptional transcription of the fifth course in "Españoletas por la E" (fol. 7r [no. 5, mm. 68–69]).

in a register other than the one we currently associate it with (e.g., fourth course in the upper octave). Although the information supplied by these notes is not unequivocal,[18] in most cases they allow the performer to infer the course used in the original tablature. That is extremely important for the following reasons: (1) The ambivalent transcription affects not only the three lower courses of the baroque guitar but also the first and second ones, implying sometimes a deep transformation of the music as performed from the original tablature, so that it seems reasonable to warn the guitarist about this in the score itself. (2) The cue notes give the choice to the performer of selecting a different way of execution without resorting to the tablature, and this is welcome since the transcription should be self-sufficient, that is, independent of the original notational system. (3) In most cases the cue notes make it possible to distinguish between the strings reproduced from the tablature and those added by the editor; otherwise, the latter are specified in the critical notes, with the exception of *campanela* passages, as explained above.

Voicing

The transcription of chords is no less problematic. On the one hand, the baroque guitar obscures inversions to "make all chords reasonably 'stable' regardless of their voicing," as Russell states.[19] All the *alfabeto* chords (see example 4 of the introduction), indeed, are mostly dealt with by Murcia and other baroque guitarists as though they are in root position, in spite of the obvious fact that, independent of the tuning, some of them are actually in first or second inversion. The reason for this can be found in the strum technique and, especially, in the double tuning of some courses—that is, in the ambivalent character of the baroque guitar. Nonetheless, in a modern instrument the inversions tend to be more audible.[20] Things being so, the most reasonable alternative would be to transcribe the strummed chords in root position, except where the musical context demands an inversion from a harmonic viewpoint.

This, however, lights up only one face of the coin. While it is true that the baroque guitar rendered the inversions acceptable, that is not to say that they remained unnoticed by Murcia's contemporaries. The frequent use of the perfect fourth from the bass (i.e., the second inversion) was often mentioned as an imperfection of this instrument at least from the seventeenth century on, as proven by Nicolás Doici's complaint in 1640.[21] Nevertheless, Nasarre, in 1723, supported his theory that the fourth was not totally a dissonance based on its frequent use in the guitar and other instruments "in place of the fifth" (i.e., in place of root position).[22] Hence the fourth from the bass was considered as a feature characteristic of baroque guitar music.

"Cifras selectas de guitarra" sometimes shows a deliberate use of second-inversion chords in a very noticeable way. In fact, a chord that was root-positioned in the sung version of "La Azucena"[23] appears in second inversion in Murcia's "La Azucena por la E," no. 37, measure 17. The same chord is plucked in measure 65, and we also find it in "Pavanas por la E," no. 4, measure 70 (example 8). Since it involves only the three upper courses, there is nothing that renders the inversion more subtle on a baroque guitar than on a modern one; no "perceptual" argument supports the transcription of that chord in root position in spite of its use as such in the piece. Of course, root position would be more "appropriate" from a harmonic point of view, but Murcia's music also lacks this sort of appropiateness in other places where no change is possible, which suggests that these devices are an integral part of his style.[24] One has the impression, once again, that their complete removal would result in the loss of some legitimate traits of his music.

For all these reasons, I have adopted the following criteria: (1) I have transcribed all the chords of the *alfabeto* system in root position, including both those indicated as such and those notated with arabic numbers (e.g., "Marionas por la B," no. 2, m. 12, fol. 2r);[25] the occasional modification of this policy is motivated by the voice-leading in the bass and specified in the critical notes. (2) Other chords notated with arabic numbers have generally been transcribed keeping the apparent inversion in the baroque guitar (e.g., "Marionas por la B," no. 2, m. 24, fol. 2r); they have only been modified where the voice-leading of the bass made such practice unacceptable (e.g., "El Amor por la E," no. 8, mm. 39–40, fol. 10r), or in the case of ending chords; when the alteration consists of an addition of notes it is specified by the use of brackets, while their removal is mentioned in the critical notes.

A somewhat problematic aspect in chords notated with arabic numbers concerns the open courses, since Murcia never specifies them by a *0* (the only exception is "El torneo por la C," no. 36, m. 5, fol. 29v). While it is evident that the open courses corresponding to the upper and inner notes must be strummed as well (they always concord with the chord's harmony), in many cases the lower open courses must be avoided (e.g., "Marionas por la B," no. 2, m. 8, fol. 2r). Consequently, I have adopted as

Example 8. Second-inversion chords: "La Azucena por la E" (fol. 31v [no. 37, mm. 17–18 and 65]) and "Pavanas por la E" (fol. 6r [no. 4, m. 70]).

a general policy to not include the lower open courses in the transcription of chords, indicating the exceptions as notes in brackets. The choice of adding such courses when they are consonant is left to the performer. Obviously, the inner and upper open courses have been added without further comments.

Finally, the sixth string of the modern guitar has been utilized occasionally to transcribe some *alfabeto* chords in root position, when such a transcription does not suppose surpassing the note A of the lower register (namely G5 and P5). Likewise, the simultaneous plucking of four courses has been used occasionally, despite its extremely exceptional character in Murcia's music (see "Notes on Performance"), to reflect the fact that, in the baroque guitar, two notes probably sounded when the third, fourth, or fifth courses were plucked. The added note appears in brackets.

Critical Notes

The critical notes report source readings that have been altered or source omissions that have been rectified in the transcriptions. As noted in the editorial policies, these include sections of works that are missing from "Cifras selectas de guitarra" but that have been supplied from other sources; fingerings and *barré* indications of "Cifras" that have been altered or added from other sources; rhythmic values that have been altered; string indications that have been added; *alfabeto* chords that have been transcribed in other than root position; and notes that have been removed from the source. Locations within each piece are identified by the measure numbers of the transcriptions. Notes are identified by position, value, or pitch (using the system in which c' = middle C) within the measure, often by referring, for convenience, to quarter-note beats in simple meters (e.g., 3/4, C) and dotted-quarter-note beats in compound meters (e.g., 6/8, 9/8). When notes are numbered this is done consecutively within a measure or beat. Chords are also referred to as appropriate.

1. Jácaras por la E

M. 42, beat 2, only the chord is *barré* (not the following 16th note).   M. 49, beat 2, only the 16th notes are *barré* (not the initial chord).

2. Marionas por la B

M. 6, for technical reasons I did not transpose the bass up to the a.   M. 23, beats 1 and 2 are spanned by two slurs below the staff, but their meaning is unknown to me.   M. 42, beat 1, the index finger is indicated for the bass (f).   M. 45, the left-hand fingering cuts the bass but is identical in "Cifras selectas" and "Códice Saldívar" (fol. 4r).   M. 71, trill indicated from e♮'.   M. 74, an extra 16th-note g at the end of the measure has been removed.   M. 76, beat 3, third 16th note, d' on the second course has been interpreted as a copy mistake and removed.

4. Pavanas por la E

M. 12, beat 2, g' is fingered with the index finger.   Mm. 21 and 25, the fingering has been modified in order to respect the presumed voice-leading.   M. 43, beat 1, d' is indicated on the fifth course.   M. 75, beat 3, the letter *O* of the *alfabeto* has been transcribed in first inversion.   M. 77, beat 2, slur spans only notes 1–3 in the manuscript.   M. 78, slurs 2 and 3 have been adapted to the transcription.

5. Españoletas por la E

M. 12, the left-hand fingering is the same in "Códice Saldívar" (fol. 6r).   M. 16, parallel fifths are not exceptional in Murcia's music.   M. 23, double-thin barline lacking.

6. Folías españolas por la E

M. 5, the left-hand fingering has been replaced by that of "Códice Saldívar" (fol. 21v) because of its greater coherence with the voice-leading.   M. 53, the left-hand fingering comes from "Códice Saldívar" (fol. 22v).   M. 76, the manuscript indicates an oblique line through notes 1–3 in order to emphasize the *campanela* effect.

7. Jácaras francesas por la D

M. 9, the first variation is repeated from this measure on, but with less strummed chords; it might indicate a *forte/piano* effect.   M. 37, the last note is g♯', but "Códice Saldívar" (fol. 30r) proves it to be a copy mistake.   M. 54 shows the impossibility of removing all the octave displacements in the transcription.

8. El Amor por la E

M. 29, beat 3, dotted quarter note in the manuscript.   M. 39, beat 1, the pitch a on the fourth course has been removed from this chord.   M. 40, beat 1, the pitch g on the fourth course has been removed from this chord.

9. Tarantelas por la E

M. 1, beat 2, the index finger is indicated for the bass (e); the middle finger comes from "Códice Saldívar" (fol. 19r).   M. 10, the left-hand fingering and strings have been adapted to the transcription.

10. Las vacas por la E

M. 3 is lacking and has been taken from "Códice Saldívar" (fol. 24r).   M. 90, note 3 is c', but it seems that the copyist mistook the first course for the second; the pitch f' is confirmed by "Códice Saldívar" (fol. 26r).

11. Folías despacio al estilo de Italia

M. 53, the added bar implies the trill is fingered 4-1, instead of 4-2 as indicated in the manuscript.   M. 59, beat 2, the 16th note is on the second course, and beat 3, note 1 is on the fourth; exceptionally, the second course has been transcribed in the upper octave. M. 76, dotted 8th note is indicated above beat 2. M. 77, slur lacking. M. 88, the appoggiatura is notated as two independent notes. M. 96, slur lacking. M. 146, the slurred notes are a–g but, by analogy with m. 154, it is evident that the copyist mistook the fourth course for the third. M. 194, the particular left-hand fingering might reflect a tendency to avoid the ring finger, pointed out by Luis Gásser, "Murcia, Santiago de," in *DMEH*, 7:898. M. 223, beat 3, the middle finger is indicated for the bass (a). M. 239, 16th note is lacking above note 2. M. 255, 16th note is lacking above beat 2, note 2. M. 265 is *barré*, but the left-hand fingering makes it unnecessary. Mm. 266–67 are entirely spanned by a bar.

12. Pasacalles de compasillo por la E

M. 10, beat 1, the chord, corresponding to the letter *O* of the *alfabeto*, has been transcribed in first inversion. M. 14, beat 4, the index finger is indicated for the bass (B♮); the middle finger comes from "Passacalles y obras" (fol. 23v). M. 15, the left-hand fingering is the same in "Passacalles y obras" (fol. 24r). M. 29, beat 4, middle finger prescribed.

13. A proporción por este tono

M. 25, beat 1, the pitch g on the fourth course has been removed from this chord. M. 59, the left-hand fingering has been adapted to the transcription.

14. Villanos por la C

M. 13, d' is on the fifth course. M. 21, beat 1, d' is on the fifth course.

16. Paradetas por la C

M. 43, beat 1, the quarter note lacks the dot. M. 54, trill indicated from c♯'. M. 76, barline lacking. Mm. 98–99, on the evident copy mistake in these measures, see example 3 of the introduction.

17. Canarios por la C

M. 66, a bar has been removed in order to adapt the passage to the transcription.

24. Otro [Menuet]

M. 3, last note, ring finger prescribed. M. 12, upper voice, little finger prescribed.

28. Otro [Menuet]

M. 23, beat 1, the pitch a is indicated on the fifth course in the manuscript.

30. Otro [Menuet]

M. 3, it seems unlikely that Murcia maintained the bass more than a quarter note given the extension it demanded to the left hand.

34. Otro [Menuet]

M. 8, chord is dotted half note.

35. Jácaras de la costa

M. 1, left-hand fingering added by the editor. M. 32, left-hand fingering taken from "Códice Saldívar" (fol. 40r). M. 37, left-hand fingering added by the editor. Mm. 41–42, the slurs have been adapted to the transcription.

36. El torneo por la C

Mm. 14, 15, and 18, on this fingering see example 3. M. 21, a *segno* has been removed, since the complex repetition of this piece has been written out. M. 38, the editorial directive of going to the last subsection is implicit in the name "Últimas reverencias" (Last reverences, m. 54); yet it is possible that the "Batallas" were performed two times followed by the "Reverencias" and a third time followed by the "Últimas reverencias," as in the "Libro de diferentes cifras" (pp. 80–83); but the manuscript is not clear on this point. M. 46, beat 2, the tablature indicates dotted 8th note; beat 3, quarter note. M. 47, the manuscript indicates the return to m. 21 by its incipit (two first chords) and a *segno*, but I have preferred to write out this fragment (mm. 47–53). M. 54, the addition of the chord is necessary to connect the "Batallas" and "Últimas reverencias"; the solution is similar to "Libro de diferentes cifras" (p. 82).

37. La Azucena por la E

M. 8, the trill from b♮' produces an unusual effect, but it is repeated in m. 32. M. 52, the fingering and string have been adapted to the transcription. M. 56, repeat sign lacking.

38. Los imposibles por la D

M. 1, only piece in the manuscript beginning with a strummed introduction. M. 59, the extant setting stops here because folio 33 is missing. M. 60, I have repeated m. 52. Mm. 61–64, these measures are taken from a similar variation in "Códice Saldívar" (fol. 14r).

39. Cumbé por la A

Since the beginning is missing with folio 33, the upbeat and mm. 1–3 have been taken from the first variation in "Códice Saldívar" (fol. 43r), excluding the strummed introduction. M. 1, although the time signature Z indicates a triple meter, the piece shows an alternation between $\frac{3}{4}$ and $\frac{6}{8}$; I transcribe the piece in $\frac{3}{4}$, showing the difference by means of the beams and rhythmic organization within each measure. M. 12, beat 2, through m. 16, beat 1, according to the repeat signs, this variation is the only one played a single time, but it is not clear whether these signs were consistently placed by the copyist. M. 20, g' is on the fourth course. M. 42, left-hand fingering taken from "Códice Saldívar" (fol. 44r). M. 44, repeat sign added by the editor. M. 45, left-hand fingering taken from "Códice Saldívar" (fol. 44r). M. 51, left-hand fingering taken from m. 42.

40. Zarambeques por la C

Mm. 2–3, left-hand fingering taken from "Códice Saldívar" (fol. 45r). M. 39, note 2 of the bass voice is g (open third course). M. 57, the pitch e on the fifth course has been removed from chord 2. M. 60, the chord has quarter-note value. M. 62, the original chord is *H7* (E major); this has been changed to *H5* (D major).

41. Obra por la C

Alemanda

M. 9, the open course is not the fourth, as suggested by the cue note, but the third; however, it is evident that the copyist mistook the fourth course for the third.

Correnta

M. 16, chord 1 has half-note value. M. 35, the rhythmic figure above the tablature staff is half note.

42. Bailad caracoles por la C

M. 9, the duplets are common in this piece. M. 54, d' is on the fifth course.

43. Marsellas por la B

Unless the contrary is indicated, the left-hand fingering in this piece comes from "Códice Saldívar" (fols. 56v–60v). M. 52, the accidental is suggested because the trill, in the next measure, is indicated from b♭. M. 63, the bar is taken from "Códice Saldívar" (fol. 58v).

46. Marcha valona

M. 11, chord 1 has dotted-half-note value.

47. Marcha de los carabineros

M. 20, last note is d (open fourth course) in the manuscript, but I think the copyist mistook the fifth course for the fourth. M. 35, one of the few evidences of a correction by the copyist, who changed a number 4 from the third to the fourth course (fol. 41r, penultimate note).

48. Marcha de las guardias de la Reina Ana

M. 12, the piece ends here because folio 42 is missing; since I have not found concordances for this march, I have completed it freely on the basis of the motives of the first section and the cadence types used by Murcia.

49. Paspied nuevo

Mm. 1–16 have been taken from both *Resumen de acompañar* (p. 57) and "Códice Saldívar" (fol. 79v), since the beginning is missing along with folio 42.

50. Burée por la D

M. 3, beat 3, although the chord corresponds to the letter *D* of the *alfabeto*, I transcribe it in second inversion. M. 11, beat 1, in the chord, the g of the transcription is f in the manuscript. M. 13, the pitch d on the fifth course has been removed in each chord; in chord 5, the stemmed note indicating the strum direction points up and down at the same time. M. 14, chords 2–3, the pitch e on the fifth course has been removed.

51. Gavota

Mm. 1 and 5, chord 1, slur below the staff; it might indicate to pluck the chord with the thumb, as prescribed by Jean Baptiste de Castillion, "Recueil des pièces de guitarre" (1730; facsimile edition in vol. 1 of *Thesaurus musicus nova series*, series A, Brussels: Alamire, 1979), 15. Mm. 3 and 17, beat 3, although the chord corresponds to the letter *D* of the *alfabeto*, I transcribe it in second inversion. M. 7, notes 1–2 are slurred. M. 8, in the chords after the double-thin barline, g' is indicated on the fourth course. M. 11, beat 2, the manuscript seems to prescribe the slur from f♯' to e'; since this is impossible for technical reasons, it must be due to the lack of space to indicate it from d♯' to e', as done in the transcription.

52. Gavota

M. 2, the left-hand fingering is taken from "Passacalles y obras" (fol. 109r). M. 6, unlike the first section, the second begins on the downbeat; the incoherence could be due to the fact that Le Cocq's version is written in $\frac{2}{4}$ time (cf. table 2 in the appendix of the introduction). M. 7, beat 1, slur below the staff; on its possible meaning for the performance of the chord, see the note to the previous piece, mm. 1 and 5; from beat 4 onwards this piece has been completed on the basis of "Passacalles y obras" (fols. 109r–109v), given that folio 44 of "Cifras" is missing. Mm. 14–15, these measures are not included in Le Cocq's version; triplets notated with 16th notes in "Passacalles y obras." M. 17, dotted quarter note in the version of "Passacalles y obras," of which the second section begins on the upbeat.

53. Idea nueva, y obra especial de clarines

The title of the suite is given in the table of contents; the left-hand fingering has been taken from "Passacalles y obras" (fols. 58r–66v).

Idea nueva de clarines primorosos por la C

Mm. 7 and 33, the rhythmic figure above the tablature staff is lacking.

Marcha

M. 5, note 2 lacks the 16th note above the tablature staff (cf. "Passacalles y obras," fol. 65r). M. 41, the rhythmic figure above the tablature staff is lacking.

Canción de ecos

M. 8, note 1, the rhythmic figure above the tablature staff is quarter note.

Fajina

There is no separation between this piece and the previous one, but its status as an independent movement is confirmed by "Passacalles y obras" (fol. 66v). M. 1, two *segnos* indicate to repeat this section; these are replaced by a repeat sign. M. 8, the rhythmic figure above the tablature staff is lacking.

Idea de dos clarines

M. 11, the dots are indicated on both sides of the half double barline, but I have assumed in the transcription that only the first section should be repeated. M. 50, note 6 is 8th note, note 8 is 16th note; the emendations are confirmed by "Passacalles y obras" (fol. 61r).

54. *Obra por la K3*

Preludio por la K3 que es lo mismo que la L

M. 4, beat 3, upper voice, note is b♭, but it is evident that the copyist mistook the second course for the third; the pitch d′ is confirmed by "Passacalles y obras" (fol. 124v) and François Campion, *Nouvelles découvertes sur la guitarre* (1705; facsimile edition, with an introduction by François Lesure, Geneva: Minkoff Reprint, 1977), 50.

Alemanda

M. 1, beat 3, the a♮′ indicated as the upper auxiliary note of the trill seems to be a copy mistake; since the performer will probably tend to play a♭′, I omit any indication in the score. M. 7, beat 3, the pitch c on the fifth course has been removed from this chord. M. 12, d′ is on the fifth course. Mm. 12 and 26, the presence of an 8th rest at the end of both sections strengthens the hypothesis that Murcia or his copyist copied (or had a copy made of) this suite directly from Campion's edition, since in other similar contexts (e.g., the "Correnta" of "Obra por la C," no. 41, m. 16, last measure of fol. 36r) only the note is written down.

Correnta

M. 1, beat 5, the upper auxiliary note of the trill is a♮′ in the manuscript; unlike in the Alemanda, m. 1, it seems possible in this case. M. 3, left-hand fingering added by the editor in order to facilitate the execution of the second trill.

Giga

Mm. 2 and 12, beat 3, the lack of the lower note may indicate that Murcia, in this piece, used a totally re-entrant tuning (cf. example 15 of the introduction). M. 28, the last measure was unusually added by the copyist outside the staff lines.

55. *Burée*

M. 3, the left-hand fingering has been added by the editor, since Murcia uses a standardized fingering for this chord (e.g., "Pasacalles de compasillo por la E," no. 12, m. 4; an exception can be found in "Jácaras por la E," no. 1, m. 24).

56. *Pasacalles de compasillo por la O*

Unless the contrary is indicated, the left-hand fingering comes from "Passacalles y obras" (fols. 43v–45r). M. 22, beat 2, inner voice, "Passacalles y obras" prescribes the index finger, but I change it to the middle finger in order to respect the presumed voice-leading. M. 32, beat 1, the letter *O* of the *alfabeto* has been transcribed in first inversion.

57. *A proporción*

Mm. 33–35, variant of mm. 17–19. Mm. 36–39, variant of "A proporción por este tono," no. 13, mm. 4–7. M. 52, beat 1, the letter *O* of the *alfabeto* has been transcribed in first inversion. Mm. 56–59, repeat of mm. 8–11.

58. *Pasacalles de compasillo por el +*

Unless the contrary is indicated, the left-hand fingering comes from "Passacalles y obras" (fols. 4r–5v). M. 3, beat 3, bass voice, the note is placed on both the second and fifth courses. M. 10, beat 2 lacks the 8th note above the tablature staff. M. 35, left-hand fingering added by the editor.

59. *A proporción*

Mm. 26 and 31, the indicated strings differ from the tablature. M. 39, beat 3, exceptionally, the third course has been transposed an octave down.

61. *A proporción*

M. 56, beat 1, the chord is *N5*; in order to respect both the general policy about the *alfabeto* chords (see the editorial policies under "Voicing") and the presumed voice-leading, it has been transcribed in root position, in spite of the considerable structural change that such a transcription implies.

62. *Pasacalles de compasillo por la G*

Unless the contrary is indicated, the left-hand fingering comes from "Passacalles y obras" (fols. 30r–32r). M. 15, beat 4, the bar is taken from "Passacalles y obras" (fol. 30r). M. 42, trill indicated from e♮′. M. 54, beat 1, the pitch f on the fourth course has been removed from this chord. M. 64, bass voice, note 3 is d′ in the manuscript; it is clear from "Passacalles y obras" (fol. 31v), however, that the copyist mistook the third course for the second; a careful observation of the tablature shows that he or she had originally placed the number 3 on the third course but, for some unexplainable reason, changed his or her mind. M. 67, beat 1, the chord is *H* (B-flat major), but I have changed it to *H3* (C major).

63. *A proporción*

M. 1, beginning very similar to "A proporción," no. 61. M. 19, string 2 added by the editor. M. 25, left-hand fingering from "Passacalles y obras" (fol. 32v). Mm. 72–75, repeat of mm. 4–7, in a sort of recapitulation similar to that found in "A proporción," no. 57 (see above).

64. *Pasacalles de compasillo por la D*

Unless the contrary is indicated, the left-hand fingering comes from "Passacalles y obras" (fols. 20r–22r). M. 2, beat 4, in the chord, the fifth course has been interpreted and transcribed as the pitch a (instead of A) for harmonic reasons (obviously, the pitch d corresponds to the bass); the intricate strings and fingering represent the only way to perform it on a modern guitar; a slur on the third course on b–a has been removed. M. 33, beat 1 lacks the 8th note above the tablature staff. M. 48, left-hand fingering added by the editor.

65. A proporción

Unless the contrary is indicated, the left-hand fingering comes from "Passacalles y obras" (fols. 22r–23v). M. 7, beat 1, for the 8th-note a, I changed the middle finger indicated in "Passacalles y obras" to the ring finger in order to prolong the bass. Mm. 18 and 20–22, the bars are taken from "Passacalles y obras" (fol. 22v). M. 40, beat 1, the chord has 8th-note value.

66. Pasacalles aclarinados por la C a compasillo

Unless the contrary is indicated, the left-hand fingering comes from "Passacalles y obras" (fols. 13v–15v). M. 6, beat 3, ring finger added by the editor. M. 13, beat 4, the dissonance in the two chords is atypical in Murcia. Mm. 18 and 25, the bars are taken from "Passacalles y obras" (fol. 14v).

67. Pasacalles a compasillo por la H

The left-hand fingering comes from "Passacalles y obras" (fols. 33r–34v), as do the bars unless they are indicated as editorial additions in the transcription. M. 21, beat 1, the chord is N3, but I have removed the notes on the fourth and fifth courses in order to transcribe it in root position and respect the presumed voice-leading. Mm. 32 and 33, beat 1, the pitch f on the fourth course has been removed from each chord. M. 47, double-thin barline lacking.

68. A proporción

The left-hand fingering comes from "Passacalles y obras" (fols. 35r–36r), as do the bars unless they are indicated as editorial additions in the transcription. M. 21, beat 1, the pitch f on the fourth course has been removed from this chord. M. 29, the chord N3 of the *alfabeto* has been transcribed in first inversion. M. 43, the measure makes no sense as it is; I amend it according to "Passacalles y obras" (fol. 36r).

69. Pasacalles de compasillo por la A

M. 30, beat 1, the pitch g on the fourth course has been removed from this chord. M. 31, the bar is taken from "Passacalles y obras" (fol. 8r). M. 34, beat 1, the chord has quarter-note value. M. 37, beat 4, the last chord lacks the 16th note above the tablature staff. M. 39, bass voice, notes 1–2 are slurred.

70. A proporción

The left-hand fingering comes from "Passacalles y obras" (fols. 9r–10r). M. 15, the bar is taken from "Passacalles y obras" (fol. 9r). M. 24, string added by the editor. M. 39, beat 3, last 16th note, the letter A of the *alfabeto* has been transcribed in first inversion. Mm. 51–52, since folio 71 and any that followed are missing, I complete this variation from "Passacalles y obras" (fol. 10r).

Notes

1. The possibility that Murcia used two strings in the first course, as explained in note 258 of the introduction, does not affect the validity of the tunings presented in example 1, since in this case the two strings would both be pitched at e′. For an exhaustive synthesis of the history of the baroque guitar, see James Tyler and Paul Sparks, *The Guitar and Its Music from the Renaissance to the Classical Era* (Oxford and New York: Oxford University Press, 2002), 49–164.

2. Cf. *The Baroque Guitar in Spain and the New World*, ed. Frank Koonce (Pacific, Mo.: Mel Bay Publications, 2006), 7.

3. Cf. Neil D. Pennington, "The Development of Baroque Guitar Music in Spain, Including a Commentary on and a Transcription of Santiago de Murcia's 'Passacalles y obras' (1732)" (Ph.D. diss., University of Maryland, 1979), 2:1–352; and *The Baroque Guitar in Spain*, 26.

4. *The Baroque Guitar in Spain*, 19, 25.

5. See Pablo Nasarre, *Escuela música según la práctica moderna* (Zaragoza: Herederos de Diego Larumbe, 1724), 1:282.

6. Unlike Frank Koonce, who specifies this with an arabic number placed to the right of the roman numeral; see *The Baroque Guitar in Spain*, 26.

7. Maurice Esses, *Dance and Instrumental Diferencias in Spain During the 17th and Early 18th Centuries* (Stuyvesant, N.Y.: Pendragon Press, 1992), 2:9.

8. *The Lute Music of Francesco Canova da Milano (1493–1543)*, ed. Arthur Ness (Cambridge, Mass. and London: Harvard University Press, 1970). Cf. Pennington, "The Development of Baroque Guitar Music in Spain," 2:iv.

9. Pennington, "The Development of Baroque Guitar Music in Spain," 2:viii–ix. This goal, perhaps legitimate when Pennington wrote his dissertation, now seems impractical and unnecessary, since baroque guitar players certainly prefer, and are able, to perform directly from tablature.

10. Santiago de Murcia, *Resumen de acompañar la parte con la guitarra* (1714; facsimile edition, with an introduction by Monica Hall, Monaco: Éditions Chanterelle, 1980), iv; Craig H. Russell, "Santiago de Murcia: Spanish Theorist and Guitarist of the Early Eighteenth Century" (Ph.D. diss., University of North Carolina at Chapel Hill, 1981), 2:xix; *Santiago de Murcia's "Códice Saldívar No. 4": A Treasury of Secular Guitar Music from Baroque Mexico*, ed. Craig H. Russell [with complete facsimile] (Urbana and Chicago: University of Illinois Press, 1995), 2:xvii.

11. As quoted by Frank Koonce in *The Baroque Guitar in Spain*, 5.

12. *Saldívar Codex No. 4* (facsimile edition, with an introduction by Michael Lorimer, Santa Barbara: n.p., 1987), xix.

13. Luis Gásser, "Murcia, Santiago de," in *Diccionario de la música española e hispanoamericana*, ed. Emilio Casares (Madrid: SGAE, 1999–2002), 7:898.

14. Russell, "Santiago de Murcia: Spanish Theorist," 1:85.

15. See Tyler and Sparks, *The Guitar and Its Music*, 111–12; Pennington, "The Development of Baroque Guitar Music in Spain," 1:118; *The Baroque Guitar in Spain*, 5.

16. Such a solution is close to that adopted in Robert de Visée, *Les deux livres de guitarre: Paris 1682 et 1686*, ed. Hélène

Charnassé, Rafael Andia, and Gérard Rebours (Paris: Éditions Transatlantiques, 1999), and Koonce in *The Baroque Guitar in Spain*, 13.

17. This is, indeed, a feature proper to any edition; see James Grier, *The Critical Editing of Music: History, Method, and Practice* (Cambridge: Cambridge University Press, 1996), 1–37.

18. In measure 59 of "Folías despacio al estilo de Italia," for instance, the unstemmed noteheads show that two notes have been transposed to the upper octave, but it is not clear if they were performed in the second, third, or fourth course.

19. *Santiago de Murcia's "Códice Saldívar No. 4,"* 2:xvii.

20. *The Baroque Guitar in Spain*, 25.

21. His *Nuevo modo de cifra*, indeed, was partly concerned with this problem; see Alejandro Vera, *Música vocal profana en el Madrid de Felipe IV: El "Libro de Tonos Humanos" (1656)* (Lleida: Institut d' Estudis Ilerdencs, 2002), 155–56.

22. Quoted in Pennington, "The Development of Baroque Guitar Music in Spain," 1:120.

23. Cf. Carmelo Caballero, *"Arded, corazón, arded": Tonos humanos del Barroco en la Península Ibérica* (Valladolid: Las Edades del Hombre, 1997), 155.

24. A typical example can be found in "Marcha valona," measure 16, where the pitch b is played on the second and third courses with a trill. That way, both the main note and the upper auxiliary note of the trill sound at the same time. In the allemande of "Obra por la K3" (m. 12) the pitch g is performed on the third and fourth courses with an appoggiatura. As a result, f♯ and g are plucked simultaneously. The most interesting thing is that Murcia does not take this ornament from Campion's version; its addition is deliberate.

25. This solution has the disadvantage that a few chords must be transcribed in the same manner, namely those represented by the letters *A* and *G3*. But the alternative of transcribing the former in first inversion and the latter in second inversion is much less convincing.

Of Related Interest

Denis Gaultier, *La Rhétorique des Dieux* and *La Rhétorique des Dieux: A Facsimile of Berlin, Staatliche Museen Preußischer Kulturbesitz, Kupferstichkabinett, MS. 78 C 12*, edited by David J. Buch, Recent Researches in the Music of the Baroque Era, 62 and 62F

Bellerofonte Castaldi, *Capricci (1622)*, edited by David Dolata, Recent Researches in the Music of the Baroque Era, 142 and 143

Songs with Theorbo (ca. 1650–1663), edited by Gordon J. Callon, Recent Researches in the Music of the Baroque Era, 105

Thomas Ford, *Lyra Viol Duets*, edited by Oleg V. Timofeyev, Recent Researches in the Music of the Baroque Era, 90

Silvius Leopold Weiss, *Lute Concerti*, reconstructed and edited by Richard Stone, Recent Researches in the Music of the Baroque Era, 136

For more information about these or any other volumes, see our website:
http://www.areditions.com/rr/

A-R Editions, Inc.
Middleton, Wisconsin
800 736-0070 (North American book orders)
608 836-9000 (phone)
608 831-8200 (fax)
http://www.areditions.com

ISBN 978-0-89579-678-3